· TROPHIES ·

Practice Book

Grade 1 ◆ Volume Two

 **Harcourt**

Orlando   Boston   Dallas   Chicago   San Diego

Visit *The Learning Site!*

www.harcourtschool.com

Contents

TIME TOGETHER – THEME 5

LESSON 1

Spelling..8
Phonics: Long Vowel: /ē/e, ea, ee...............9
Grammar: Names of Holidays..................10
Phonics: Long Vowel: /ē/e, ea, ee.............11
Vocabulary: "A Bed Full of Cats" 12
Phonics: CVVC-CVVCC Words 13
Study Skill: Alphabetize 14
Phonics: Contractions: 's, n't, 'll 15

LESSON 2

Spelling..16
Phonics: Long Vowel: /ā/a-e 17
Grammar: Using I and Me.......................18
Phonics: Long Vowel: /ā/a-e 19
Vocabulary: "Me On the Map" 20
Phonics: CVC-CVCe Words 21
Comprehension: Classify/Categorize 22
Phonics: Inflections: -ed, -ing 23

LESSON 3

Spelling..24
Phonics: Long Vowel: /ē/y.......................25
Grammar: Using He, She,
    It, They 26
Phonics: Long Vowel: /ē/y.......................27
Vocabulary: "At Home
    Around the World" 28
Phonics: CVCCy-CCVCCy Words.........29
Comprehension: Classify/Categorize 30
Phonics: Inflections: -es, -ed, -ing 31

LESSON 4

Spelling..32
Phonics: Long Vowel: /ī/i-e......................33
Grammar: Describing Words
    for Feelings...34
Phonics: Long Vowel: /ī/i-e......................35
Vocabulary: "Tell Me a Story" 36
Phonics: CVC-CVCe Words 37
Study Skill: Alphabetize 38
Phonics: Contractions: 's, n't, 'll 39

LESSON 5

Spelling..40
Phonics: Consonant: /s/c 41
Grammar: Describing Words
    for Color, Size, Shape 42
Phonics: Consonant: /s/c 43
Vocabulary: "My Robot"..........................44
Phonics: CVCe-CCVCe Words 45
Phonics: Phonograms: -ice, -ide.................46

LESSON 6

Spelling..47
Phonics: Vowel Variant: /ou/ow, ou..........48
Grammar: Describing Words
    for Taste, Smell, Sound.........................49
Phonics: Vowel Variant: /ou/ow, ou..........50
Vocabulary: "On the Job
    with Dr. Martha Smith" 51
Phonics: CCVVC Words 52
Comprehension: Classify/Categorize 53
Phonics: Phonograms: -own, -ound 54

Contents

TIME TOGETHER – THEME 5

LESSON 7

Spelling...55
Phonics: Long Vowel: /ī/y, *ie*...............56
Grammar: Describing Words:
  How Many 57
Phonics: Long Vowel: /ī/y, *ie*...............58
Vocabulary: "Little Bear's Friend"............59
Phonics: Words with *y*..........................60
Study Skill: Alphabetize 61
Phonics: Contraction: *'s, n't, 'll*............62

LESSON 8

Spelling...63
Phonics: Long Vowel: /ō/o-e 64
Grammar: Describing Words:
  Weather 65
Phonics: Long Vowel: /ō/o-e 66
Vocabulary: "Busy Buzzy Bee" 67
Phonics: CVC-CVCe words 68
Phonics: Initial Blends with *l* 69

CUT-OUT/FOLD-UP BOOKS

"Patch's Treat" 71
"Baseball" 73
"Eating Yummy Cake" 75
"One More Time" 77
"How to Make a Face" 79
"Billy Brown's Lunch" 81
"A Dream to Fly" 83
"Squirrels at Home" 85

Contents

GATHER AROUND – THEME 6

LESSON 1

Spelling...2

Phonics: Long Vowel: /ī/*igh* 3

Grammar: Describing Words
with *-er, -est* 4

Phonics: Long Vowel: /ī/*igh* 5

Vocabulary: "The Story of a Blue Bird"....6

Phonics: CVVC and *-igh* Words..............7

Comprehension: Plot.............................8

Phonics: Inflections *-ed -ing* 9

LESSON 2

Spelling...10

Phonics: Long Vowel: /ā/*ai, ay* 11

Grammar: Verbs 12

Phonics: Long Vowel: /ā/*ai, ay* 13

Vocabulary: "Frog and
Toad All Year" 14

Phonics: CVV-CVVC-CVCe Words 15

Phonics: Inflections: *-ed, -ing* 16

LESSON 3

Spelling...17

Phonics: Long Vowel: /ī/*i* 18

Grammar: Verbs That
Tell About Now 19

Phonics: Long Vowel: /ī/*i* 20

Vocabulary: "Fishing Bears"................21

Phonics: CVCe-CVCC Words 22

Comprehension: Main Idea....................23

Phonics: Inflections: *-ed, -ing* 24

LESSON 4

Spelling...25

Phonics: Long Vowel: /ō/*o* 26

Grammar: Using *Am, Is,* and *Are*............27

Phonics: Long Vowel: /ō/*o* 28

Vocabulary: "How to
Be a Nature Detective"......................29

Phonics: CVCe, CVCC Words 30

Comprehension: Main Idea.....................31

Phonics: Contractions: *'ve, 'd, 're* 32

LESSON 5

Spelling...33

Phonics: Consonant: /j/*g, dge* 34

Grammar: Verbs That Tell
About the Past.................................35

Phonics: Consonant: /j/*g, dge* 36

Vocabulary: "The Puddle" 37

Phonics: CVCe-CVCCe words 38

Comprehension: Plot............................39

Phonics: Contractions: *'ve, 'd, 're* 40

LESSON 6

Spelling...41

Phonics: Long Vowel: /(y)oo/*u-e*............42

Grammar: Using *Was* and *Were* 43

Phonics: Long Vowel: /(y)oo/*u-e*..............44

Vocabulary: "Poppleton Everyday" 45

Phonics: CVCe Words 46

Phonics: Inflections: *-ed, -ing*.............47

LESSON 7

Spelling...48

Phonics: Short Vowel: /e/*ea* 49

Grammar: Using *Go* and *Went* 50

Phonics: Short Vowel: /e/*ea* 51

Vocabulary: "Sleep Is for Everyone" 52

Phonics: CVC-CVVC Words 53

Comprehension: Main Idea....................54

Phonics: Inflections: *-ed, -ing* 55

Contents

GATHER AROUND – THEME 6

LESSON 8

Spelling...56
Phonics: Vowel Digraph: /$\overline{oo}$/oo.................57
Grammar: Contractions with *Not* 58
Phonics: Vowel Digraph: /$\overline{oo}$/oo.................59
Vocabulary: "Baboon" 60
Phonics: CVVC-CVVCC Words 61
Comprehension: Plot....................................62
Phonics: Phonograms: *-oom, -oot*...............63

CUT-OUT/FOLD-UP BOOKS

"The Long Flight".................................65
"Frog and Mouse" 67
"Find Something to Do" 69
"Old Rover" 71
"The Bridge"..73
"Three Moles and a Mule" 75
"Ready for Space"..................................77
"The Zoo Race"..................................79

SKILLS AND STRATEGIES INDEX.....................81

END-OF-SELECTION TESTS

Time Together Theme 5

"A Bed Full of Cats" A1
"Me on the Map" A5
"At Home Around the World" A9
"Tell Me a Story" A13
"My Robot"...A17
"On the Job with Dr. Martha Smith" A21
"Little Bear's Friend" A25
"Busy Buzzy Bee"................................A29

Gather Around Theme 6

"The Story of a Blue Bird".................A33
"Frog and Toad All Year"....................A37
"Fishing Bears" A41
"How to Be a Nature Detective".........A45
"The Puddle"..A49
"Poppleton Everyday" A53
"Sleep Is for Everyone" A57
"Baboon" A61

· T R O P H I E S ·

Level Four

Time Together

Name _____

▶ **Read the words. Then read the name of each group. Write each word in the group where it belongs.**

Words With Long e	Words With Long o
_____	_____
_____	_____
_____	_____
_____	_____
_____	
_____	**Words Without**
_____	**Long o or Long e**
_____	_____
_____	_____
_____	_____

Spelling Words

me
mean
bean
be
beet
feet
low
road
who
door

© Harcourt

FLORIDA BENCHMARK LA.B.1.1.3: The student produces final simple documents that have been edited for correct spelling; appropriate end punctuation; correct capitalization of initial words, "I," and names of people; correct sentence structure; and correct usage of age-appropriate verb/subject and noun/pronoun agreement.

8

Practice Book
Time Together • Lesson 1

▶ **Write a word from the box that tells about each picture. Use each word only once.**

we	see	eat	read	me

1.

_____

- - - - - - - - - - - - - - -

_____

2.

_____

- - - - - - - - - - - - - - -

_____

3.

_____

- - - - - - - - - - - - - - -

_____

4.

_____

- - - - - - - - - - - - - - -

_____

5.

_____

- - - - - - - - - - - - - - -

_____

© Harcourt

FLORIDA BENCHMARK LA.A.1.1.2: The student identifies words and constructs meaning from text, illustrations, graphics, and charts using the strategies of phonics, word structure, and context clues.

9

Practice Book
Time Together • Lesson 1

Name _____

► **Write the name of the holiday that matches each clue. Begin each holiday name with a capital letter.**

valentine's day	new year's day	thanksgiving day

1. This is the first day of the year!

_____

- - - - - - - - - - - - - - - - - - -

_____

2. We make cards for friends. We use red.

_____

- - - - - - - - - - - - - - - - - - -

_____

3. We give thanks on this day.

_____

- - - - - - - - - - - - - - - - - - -

_____

 TRY THIS Write about your favorite holiday. Draw a picture to go with your story.

FLORIDA BENCHMARK LA.B.1.1.3: The student produces final simple documents that have been edited for correct spelling; appropriate end punctuation; correct capitalization of initial words, "I," and names of people; correct sentence structure; and correct usage of age-appropriate verb/subject and noun/pronoun agreement.

10

Practice Book
Time Together • Lesson 1

© Harcourt

Name _____

► **Look at each picture. Write the word from the box that completes the sentence.**

green	bee	eat	seat	me	feet

1.

The cat is on the _____.

2.

She sees the _____.

3.

She lands on her _____.

4.

She wants to _____.

5.

Her rug is _____.

6.

She comes to _____.

FLORIDA BENCHMARK LA.A.1.1.2: The student identifies words and constructs meaning from text, illustrations, graphics, and charts using the strategies of phonics, word structure, and context clues.

Practice Book
Time Together • Lesson 1

© Harcourt

Name _____

▶ **Finish the story. Write a word from the box to complete each sentence.**

should	room	anything	write	know
only		moved	also	those

_____

1. Oh, no! I can't find _____!

_____

2. Do you _____ where my bat is?

_____

3. I have _____

one shoe. I should look for those shirts.

_____

4. I think I _____ them up here.

_____

5. I will write a note to clean my _____.

FLORIDA BENCHMARK LA.A.1.1.3: The student uses knowledge of appropriate grade-, age-, and developmental-level vocabulary in reading.

12

Practice Book
Time Together • Lesson 1

© Harcourt

Name _____

▶ **Write the words where they belong in the puzzle.**

beach   bows   coat   feet   toast   weeks

1.

4.

2.

5.

3.

6.

4.↓

5.↓

6.↓

1.→

2.→

3.→

FLORIDA BENCHMARK LA.A.1.1.2: The student identifies words and constructs meaning from text, illustrations, graphics, and charts using the strategies of phonics, word structure, and context clues.

13

Practice Book
Time Together • Lesson 1

Name _____

▶ **Put the words in ABC order. One has been done for you in each set.**

fish   yell   pond
duck

1. _____

2. _____

3. _____

4. _yell_

wag   happy   play   bark

1. _____

2. _happy_

3. _____

4. _____

FLORIDA BENCHMARK LA.A.2.1.5: The student uses simple
materials of the reference system to obtain information.

14

Practice Book
Time Together • Lesson 1

Name _____

► **Read each sentence. Combine the two words to form a contraction. Write the contraction to complete the sentence.**

She is

_____

- - - - - - - - - - - - - - - - - -

1. _____ getting lots of nuts.

He is

_____

- - - - - - - - - - - - - - - - - -

2. _____ helping a lot.

do not

_____

- - - - - - - - - - - - - - - - - -

3. They _____ eat them all now.

They will

_____

- - - - - - - - - - - - - - - - - -

4. _____ put the nuts away for winter.

© Harcourt

FLORIDA BENCHMARK LA.A.1.1.2: The student identifies words and constructs meaning from text, illustrations, graphics, and charts using the strategies of phonics, word structure, and context clues.

15

Practice Book
Time Together • Lesson 1

▶ **Read the words. Then read the name of each group. Write each word in the group where it belongs.**

Words With Long <u>a</u>	Words With Long <u>e</u>
_____	_____
_____	_____
_____	_____
_____	_____
_____	_____
_____	**Words With Long <u>o</u>**
_____	_____
_____	_____
_____	_____

Spelling Words

came
game
gate
late
lake
take
feet
me
know
also

FLORIDA BENCHMARK LA.B.1.1.3: The student produces final simple documents that have been edited for correct spelling; appropriate end punctuation; correct capitalization of initial words, "I," and names of people; correct sentence structure; and correct usage of age-appropriate verb/subject and noun/pronoun agreement.

16

Practice Book
Time Together • Lesson 2

Name _____

▶ **Write the word that best completes
each sentence.**

came	game	made	make	take

_____

- - - - - - - - - - - - -

1. Come play a _____ with us.

_____

- - - - - - - - - - - - -

2. We need to _____ a team.

_____

- - - - - - - - - - - - -

3. We _____ to show you this map.

_____

- - - - - - - - - - - - -

4. We _____ it.

_____

- - - - - - - - - - - - -

5. It will be faster if you _____ the bus
with us.

**TRY
THIS** Write a two-line poem about a game you like. Use
Spelling Words in your poem.

FLORIDA BENCHMARK LA.A.1.1.2: The student identifies words and
constructs meaning from text, illustrations, graphics, and charts
using the strategies of phonics, word structure, and context clues.

17

Practice Book
Time Together • Lesson 2

► **Read the story and complete each sentence with the word I or me.**

_____

_____ like to go to the park with Dan. We

_____   _____

swing. Dan will push _____. Then _____ push

_____

him. We play ball. _____ kick the ball to Dan. He

_____   _____

kicks the ball to _____. We climb. _____ go up to

_____

the top. _____ like to play at the park.

FLORIDA BENCHMARK LA.B.1.1.3: The student produces final simple documents that have been edited for correct spelling; appropriate end punctuation; correct capitalization of initial words, "I," and names of people; correct sentence structure; and correct usage of age-appropriate verb/subject and noun/pronoun agreement.

18

© Harcourt

Name _____

▶ **Write the word from the box that completes each sentence. Then read the story.**

| Take | cake | gave | Kate | game | ate |

The Surprise

_____   _____

_____ is my friend. She _____

_____

me a map. "_____ this map, and find the

surprise." I walked all around the house.

_____

The _____ was fun. The surprise

_____

was a birthday _____.

_____

We _____ some cake.

FLORIDA BENCHMARK LA.A.1.1.2: The student identifies words and constructs meaning from text, illustrations, graphics, and charts using the strategies of phonics, word structure, and context clues.

19

Practice Book
Time Together • Lesson 2

© Harcourt

Name _____

▶ **Write the word in the box that best completes each sentence.**

| country | Earth | over | special | world | town |

_____

1. "You are not from this _____!" said Max.

_____

2. "You are right, _____
   boy. What is this town?" it asked.

_____

3. "This is our _____,
   the U.S.A." said Beth.

_____

4. "What is _____ there?" it asked.
   "That is our house," said Beth.

_____

5. What a _____ visit!

FLORIDA BENCHMARK LA.A.1.1.3: The student uses knowledge of
appropriate grade-, age-, and developmental-level vocabulary in
reading.

Practice Book
Time Together • Lesson 2

© Harcourt

▶ **Write the words where they belong in the puzzle.**

| cape | cane | map | maze | pat | tap | cake |

1.

2.

3.

4.

5.

6.

7.

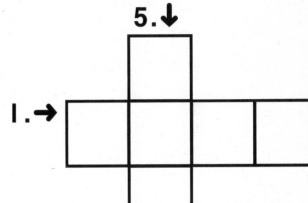

FLORIDA BENCHMARK LA.A.1.1.2: The student identifies words and constructs meaning from text, illustrations, graphics, and charts using the strategies of phonics, word structure, and context clues.

21

Practice Book
Time Together • Lesson 2

© Harcourt

Name _____

▶ **Read the words. Then read the name of each group. Write each word in the correct group.**

tree   rock   dog

block   mop   fish

Things That Grow	Things That Do Not Grow
_____	_____
_____	_____
_____	_____
_____	_____
_____	_____
_____	_____

FLORIDA BENCHMARK LA.A.1.1.3: The student uses knowledge of appropriate grade-, age-, and developmental-level vocabulary in reading.

22

Practice Book
Time Together • Lesson 2

© Harcourt

Name _____

▶ **Read the word above each line. Add -ed or -ing to the word to complete the sentence.**

1.

skate
_____

- - - - - - - - - - - - - -

We _____
on the path.

2.

make
_____

- - - - - - - - - - - - - -

He is _____
drinks for us.

3.

chase
_____

- - - - - - - - - - - - - -

The dog is _____
a ball.

4.

bake
_____

- - - - - - - - - - - - - -

They _____
a cake.

FLORIDA BENCHMARK LA.A.1.1.2: The student identifies words and constructs meaning from text, illustrations, graphics, and charts using the strategies of phonics, word structure, and context clues.

23

Practice Book
Time Together • Lesson 2

▶ **Read the words. Then read the name of each group. Write each word in the group where it belongs.**

Words With y

_____   _____
_____   _____
_____   _____
_____   _____
_____   _____

Words With a

_____   _____
_____   _____

Words Without y and a

_____   _____
_____   _____

Spelling Words

jelly

belly

bunny

funny

furry

hurry

take

came

world

over

© Harcourt

FLORIDA BENCHMARK LA.B.1.1.3: The student produces final simple documents that have been edited for correct spelling; appropriate end punctuation; correct capitalization of initial words, "I," and names of people; correct sentence structure; and correct usage of age-appropriate verb/subject and noun/pronoun agreement.

24

Practice Book
Time Together • Lesson 3

Name _____

▶ **Write the word in the box that best completes the sentence.**

any	Betsy	many	very	funny

_____

1. I have _____ books to read.

_____

2. Some books are _____ big.

_____

3. I read to _____.

_____

4. Some stories are really _____.

_____

5. I do not have _____ more books.

FLORIDA BENCHMARK LA.A.1.1.2: The student identifies words and constructs meaning from text, illustrations, graphics, and charts using the strategies of phonics, word structure, and context clues.

25

Practice Book
Time Together • Lesson 3

© Harcourt

Name _____

▶ **Use a word from the box to complete each sentence. Circle the noun that the new word tells about.**

They	he	She	it

1. Is Tom home?

_____

- - - - - - - - - -

Can _____ play with us?

2. Will Tom bring a bat?

_____

- - - - - - - - - -

He will bring _____ to play ball.

3. Bill and Pam will come, too.

_____

- - - - - - - - - -

_____ will meet us at the park.

4. Mom will bring us home.

_____

- - - - - - - - - -

_____ can bring Tom home, too.

FLORIDA BENCHMARK LA.B.1.1.3: The student produces final simple documents that have been edited for correct spelling; appropriate end punctuation; correct capitalization of initial words, "I," and names of people; correct sentence structure; and correct usage of age-appropriate verb/subject and noun/pronoun agreement.

26

Practice Book
Time Together • Lesson 3

© Harcourt

Name _____

▶ **Read the story. Circle the words with the vowel sound /ē/, spelled _y_. Then write the words.**

My little brother Billy is fussy. He gets cranky if his bunny is not with him. I think the bunny is funny. Billy looks silly with his bunny, but it makes him happy.

1. _____

2. _____

3. _____

4. _____

5. _____

6. _____

7. _____

 TRY THIS Draw a picture of Billy's bunny. Write a sentence about your picture.

© Harcourt

FLORIDA BENCHMARK LA.A.1.1.2: The student identifies words and constructs meaning from text, illustrations, graphics, and charts using the strategies of phonics, word structure, and context clues.

Name _____

▶ **Read the words in the box. Write the word that answers each clue.**

above	hold	water	old	different	years	warm

1. You can drink it.

___ ___ ___ ___ ___

___ ___ ___ ___ ___

_____

2. It's not too hot. It's _____.

___ ___ ___ ___

___ ___ ___ ___

_____

3. It's not the same. It's _____.

___ ___ ___ ___ ___ ___ ___ ___ ___

___ ___ ___ ___ ___ ___ ___ ___ ___

_____

4. You do this with your hands.

___ ___ ___ ___

___ ___ ___ ___

_____

5. Look up _____ you.

___ ___ ___ ___ ___

___ ___ ___ ___ ___

In two years we will fly in a plane like that.

FLORIDA BENCHMARK LA.A.1.1.3: The student uses knowledge of appropriate grade-, age-, and developmental-level vocabulary in reading.

28

Practice Book
Time Together • Lesson 3

© Harcourt

Name _____

▶ **Write the word from the box that best completes each sentence.**

| fuzzy | sticky | happy | berry | dirty | chilly |

1. When it starts to get

_____

_ _ _ _ _ _ _ _ _ _ _ _ _ _ _ _ _ _

_____ out, we

pick all the crops.

_____

_ _ _ _ _ _ _ _ _ _ _ _ _ _ _ _ _ _

2. I like the _____ peaches best.

_____

_ _ _ _ _ _ _ _ _ _ _ _ _ _ _ _ _ _

3. We like to go _____ picking.

_____

_ _ _ _ _ _ _ _ _ _ _ _ _ _ _ _ _ _

4. We wash all the _____ ones.

_____

_ _ _ _ _ _ _ _ _ _ _ _ _ _ _ _ _ _

5. Mom makes lots of _____, sweet jelly.

FLORIDA BENCHMARK LA.A.1.1.2: The student identifies words and constructs meaning from text, illustrations, graphics, and charts using the strategies of phonics, word structure, and context clues.

29

Practice Book
Time Together • Lesson 3

© Harcourt

Name _____

► **Read the words in the box. Which are pets? Which are farm animals? Write each word in the correct group.**

sheep	cat	hamster	hen
goat	bird	pig	fish

Pets   **Farm Animals**

_____   _____

_____   _____

_____   _____

_____   _____

_____   _____

_____   _____

_____   _____

FLORIDA BENCHMARK LA.A.1.1.3: The student uses knowledge of appropriate grade-, age-, and developmental-level vocabulary in reading.

Practice Book
Time Together • Lesson 3

© Harcourt

Name _____

▶ **Write the word that completes each sentence.**

crying   cried

_ _ _ _ _ _ _ _ _ _

1. "The tree is too wet!" he _____.

drying   dries

_ _ _ _ _ _ _ _ _ _

2. He waited. The sun is _____ up the rain.

tries   tried

_ _ _ _ _ _ _ _ _ _

3. Now he _____ to climb the tree.

hurries   hurrying

_ _ _ _ _ _ _ _ _ _

4. He _____ up to the treehouse.

© Harcourt

FLORIDA BENCHMARK LA.A.1.1.2: The student identifies words and constructs meaning from text, illustrations, graphics, and charts using the strategies of phonics, word structure, and context clues.

31

Practice Book
Time Together • Lesson 3

Name _____

▶ **Read the words. Then read the name of each group. Write each word in the group where it belongs.**

Words With Long i

_____

- -

_____

_____

- -

_____

Words With Long e Spelled y

_____

- -

_____

_____

- -

Other Words

_____

- -

_____

_____

- -

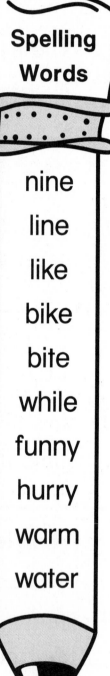

Spelling Words

nine
line
like
bike
bite
while
funny
hurry
warm
water

© Harcourt

FLORIDA BENCHMARK LA.B.1.1.3: The student produces final simple documents that have been edited for correct spelling; appropriate end punctuation; correct capitalization of initial words, "I," and names of people; correct sentence structure; and correct usage of age-appropriate verb/subject and noun/pronoun agreement.

32

Practice Book
Time Together • Lesson 4

Name _____

► **Solve each riddle. Write the words in the puzzle.**

hide   bike   smile   white   slide   time

1.	snow is this	
2.	use a clock to tell _ _ _ _	
3.	two-wheeler	
4.	seen on a happy person	
5.	go down the _ _ _ _ _	
6.	_ _ _ _ and seek	

FLORIDA BENCHMARK LA.A.1.1.2: The student identifies words and constructs meaning from text, illustrations, graphics, and charts using the strategies of phonics, word structure, and context clues.

33

Practice Book
Time Together • Lesson 4

© Harcourt

Name _____

▶ **Look at the pictures and write a word that describes the feeling.**

| happy | hungry | sad | surprised | sleepy |

1. _____

2. _____

3. _____

4. _____

5. _____

FLORIDA BENCHMARK LA.B.1.1.2: The student drafts and revises simple sentences and passages, stories, letters and simple explanations that express ideas clearly; show an awareness of topic and audience; have a beginning, middle, and ending; effectively use common words; have supporting detail; and are in legible printing.

34

Practice Book
Time Together • Lesson 4

© Harcourt

▶ **Read the questions. Circle the answers.**

1. What is six plus three?

   time   **nine**

2. What has two wheels?

   bike   **like**

3. What can you do on a bus or in a car?

   ride   **nine**

4. What do you want to know when you look at a clock?

   bike   **time**

5. How do you feel about a friend?

   ride   **like**

 TRY THIS Draw a picture of one of the words. Write the word under your picture.

FLORIDA BENCHMARK LA.A.1.1.2: The student identifies words and constructs meaning from text, illustrations, graphics, and charts using the strategies of phonics, word structure, and context clues.

35

Practice Book
Time Together • Lesson 4

© Harcourt

Name _____

▶ **Read the words in the box. Write each word in the sentence where it belongs.**

cook	because	Young	most	Why	front

1. _____ don't you

   listen to me?

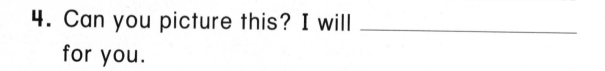

2. It's _____ you're so young.

3. Sit in _____ of this.

4. Can you picture this? I will _____

   for you.

5. You should eat _____ of it.

FLORIDA BENCHMARK LA.A.1.1.3: The student uses knowledge of appropriate grade-, age-, and developmental-level vocabulary in reading.

36

Practice Book
Time Together • Lesson 4

© Harcourt

Name _____

▶ **Unscramble each picture name. Then write the word.**

1.   i g p

_____
- - - - - - - - - - - - - - -
_____

2.  k e b i

_____
- - - - - - - - - - - - - - -
_____

3.   e m i d

_____
- - - - - - - - - - - - - - -
_____

4.  t i h

_____
- - - - - - - - - - - - - - -
_____

5.   e n n i

_____
- - - - - - - - - - - - - - -
_____

6.   g i w

_____
- - - - - - - - - - - - - - -
_____

7.   m e t i

_____
- - - - - - - - - - - - - - -
_____

8.   t i s

_____
- - - - - - - - - - - - - - -
_____

© Harcourt

FLORIDA BENCHMARK LA.A.1.1.2: The student identifies words and constructs meaning from text, illustrations, graphics, and charts using the strategies of phonics, word structure, and context clues.

37

Name _____

▶ **Help the children get into ABC order by their first names. Write their names in ABC order.**

Todd   Russ   Dan   Jenny

1. _____   2. _____

3. _____   4. _____

▶ **Write the robot names in ABC order.**

Whiz   Buzz   Zap   Fizz

1. _____   2. _____

3. _____   4. _____

FLORIDA BENCHMARK LA.A.2.1.5: The student uses simple
materials of the reference system to obtain information.

38

Practice Book
Time Together • Lesson 4

© Harcourt

Name _____

► **Read the chart. Then write the contraction that completes each sentence.**

She is	She's
he is	he's
do not	don't
can not	can't
I will	I'll

1. Kate is tired. _____ going to bed.

2. The cat can purr, but it _____ bark.

3. I want some cake. _____ make it.

4. Jack is late, but _____ on his way.

5. I _____ have a red hat.

FLORIDA BENCHMARK LA.A.1.1.2: The student identifies words and constructs meaning from text, illustrations, graphics, and charts using the strategies of phonics, word structure, and context clues.

39

Practice Book
Time Together • Lesson 4

© Harcourt

► **Read the words. Then read the name of each group. Write each word in the group where it belongs.**

Words With <u>i-e</u>	Words With <u>a-e</u>
_____	_____
- - - - - -	- - - - - -
_____	_____
- - - - - -	- - - - - -
_____	_____
- - - - - -	- - - - - -
_____	_____
- - - - - -	- - - - - -
_____	_____
- - - - - -	**Word With <u>y</u>**
_____	_____
- - - - - -	- - - - - -
_____	_____
- - - - - -	**Word With <u>o</u>**
_____	_____
- - - - - -	- - - - - -
	_____

Spelling Words

ice
nice
rice
race
face
space
like
nine
why
most

© Harcourt

FLORIDA BENCHMARK LA.B.1.1.3: The student produces final simple documents that have been edited for correct spelling; appropriate end punctuation; correct capitalization of initial words, "I," and names of people; correct sentence structure; and correct usage of age-appropriate verb/subject and noun/pronoun agreement.

40

Practice Book
Time Together • Lesson 5

Name _____

▶ **Write the word that best completes each sentence.**

city	space	ice	mice	nice

_____

1. A _____ is a big place.

2. Did the _____ melt yet?

3. I will blast into _____.

4. I eat fish. What do _____ eat?

5. My friends are _____.

TRY THIS Fold a piece of paper into four squares. Use four words from the box. Write one word on each square and draw a picture about each word.

FLORIDA BENCHMARK LA.A.1.1.2: The student identifies words and constructs meaning from text, illustrations, graphics, and charts using the strategies of phonics, word structure, and context clues.

41

Practice Book
Time Together • Lesson 5

Name _____

► **Read the ad. Then follow the directions.**

1. Find two color words. Color each one.

2. Find two words that tell about size.
Put a line under each one.

3. Find a word that tells about shape. Circle it.

Fred's Fish Shop

Come to my big shop.

I have small fish for

your tank. Take home a

red fish or a yellow fish.

My tank is a circle. Fish are fun!

TRY THIS Look around the classroom. Draw something you see. Write four describing words about it. Use words that tell about size, shape, and color.

FLORIDA BENCHMARK LA.B.1.1.2: The student drafts and revises simple sentences and passages, stories, letters and simple explanations that express ideas clearly; show an awareness of topic and audience; have a beginning, middle, and ending; effectively use common words; have supporting detail; and are in legible printing.

42

Practice Book
Time Together • Lesson 5

Name _____

▶ **Write the word from the box that best matches each clue.**

race	face	dance	mice	nice

1. It's fun to hear the song and move to the beat.

_____

2. This can be happy or sad.

_____

3. Someone kind and good is

_____

4. A chance to test how fast you can go

_____

5. Small animals with long tails

_____

FLORIDA BENCHMARK LA.A.1.1.2: The student identifies words and constructs meaning from text, illustrations, graphics, and charts using the strategies of phonics, word structure, and context clues.

43

Name _____

▶ **Read the words in the box. Write the word that best completes each sentence.**

always	does	sound	even
Once	pretty	say	Almost

1. I almost _____ know when to get up.

2. I say that I don't _____ need a clock!

3. I get up when I hear a _____ sound.

4. _____ I got up too late.

5. My bird clock _____ not work when it rains.

FLORIDA BENCHMARK LA.A.1.1.3: The student uses knowledge of appropriate grade-, age-, and developmental-level vocabulary in reading.

44

Practice Book
Time Together • Lesson 5

© Harcourt

Name _____

▶ **Write the words where they belong in the puzzle.**

| spice | price | laces | mice | place | slice |

1. how much something costs
2. where you are
3.

4.

5.

6.

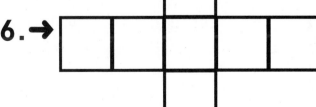

FLORIDA BENCHMARK LA.A.1.1.2: The student identifies words and constructs meaning from text, illustrations, graphics, and charts using the strategies of phonics, word structure, and context clues.

45

Practice Book
Time Together • Lesson 5

© Harcourt

Name _____

▶ **Write the word from the box that completes each sentence.**

| nice | ride | hide | mice | slide | rice |

1. We like _____.

2. We like the _____.

3. We can _____.

4. We go on a _____.

5. We are _____.

6. We are _____ mice.

FLORIDA BENCHMARK LA.A.1.1.2: The student identifies words and
constructs meaning from text, illustrations, graphics, and charts
using the strategies of phonics, word structure, and context clues.

46

Practice Book
Time Together • Lesson 5

© Harcourt

▶ **Read the words. Then read the name of each group. Write each word in the group where it belongs.**

Words With <u>ow</u>

_____ _____
_____ _____
_____ _____

Words With <u>ou</u>

_____ _____

Words Without <u>ow</u> or <u>ou</u>

_____ _____
_____ _____
_____ _____

Spelling Words

cow
how
now
down
out
round
nice
face
does
once

FLORIDA BENCHMARK LA.B.1.1.3: The student produces final simple documents that have been edited for correct spelling; appropriate end punctuation; correct capitalization of initial words, "I," and names of people; correct sentence structure; and correct usage of age-appropriate verb/subject and noun/pronoun agreement.

47

Practice Book
Time Together • Lesson 6

Name _____

▶ **Read each sentence. Draw a line under the words with the /ou/ sound as in <u>out</u>. Then draw a picture to go with each sentence.**

1. The mouse king

has a crown.

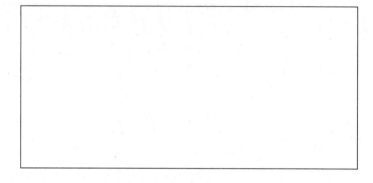

2. The clown is

under a cloud.

3. The hound dog

found a ball.

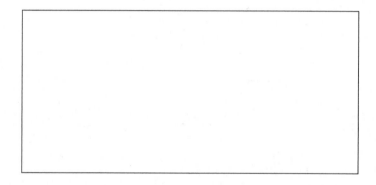

4. Mrs. Down's

house is brown.

FLORIDA BENCHMARK LA.A.1.1.2: The student identifies words and constructs meaning from text, illustrations, graphics, and charts using the strategies of phonics, word structure, and context clues.

48

Practice Book
Time Together • Lesson 6

© Harcourt

Name _____

▶ **Read the chart. Write the word from the chart that best completes each sentence.**

Taste words	Smell words	Sound words	Feel words
sweet	fresh	loud	hard
sour	rotten	soft	fluffy

1.  are _____ .

2. A _____ is _____ .

3. A _____ is _____ .

4. Hot _____ smells _____ .

5. A _____ can be _____ .

© Harcourt

FLORIDA BENCHMARK LA.B.1.1.2: The student drafts and revises simple sentences and passages, stories, letters and simple explanations that express ideas clearly; show an awareness of topic and audience; have a beginning, middle, and ending; effectively use common words; have supporting detail; and are in legible printing.

49

▶ **Read the story. Circle the words with <u>ow</u>. Draw a line under the words with <u>ou</u>. Write all the words in the chart. Write each word just one time.**

The mouse came back from town.

"How are you?" she said.

"I found a crown," said the cow.

"Where is my crown?" growled the hound dog.

The mouse and cow bowed. The king put on his crown.

ou	ow
_____	_____
_____	_____
_____	_____
_____	_____
_____	_____
_____	_____
_____	_____
	_____
	_____
	_____

FLORIDA BENCHMARK LA.A.1.1.2: The student identifies words and constructs meaning from text, illustrations, graphics, and charts using the strategies of phonics, word structure, and context clues.

50

Practice Book
Time Together • Lesson 6

© Harcourt

Name _____

▶ **Read the words in the box. Write the word that best completes each sentence.**

any	busy	care	Dr.	eight	took

_____

1. Dr. Lee is always very _____ .

_____

2. She takes _____ of animals.

_____

3. She _____ care of my dog.

_____

4. She took care of my _____ fish.

_____

5. She can help _____ animal.

FLORIDA BENCHMARK LA.A.1.1.3: The student uses knowledge of appropriate grade-, age-, and developmental-level vocabulary in reading.

51

Practice Book
Time Together • Lesson 6

© Harcourt

Name _____

► **Read each clue. Write a word from the box that tells about the clue.**

crown	cloud	growl	shout	clown

1.  Look up outside. You might see this. _____

2.  This is a hat for a queen. _____

3.  This man is funny. _____

4.  This sound is loud. _____

5.  A dog might do this. _____

FLORIDA BENCHMARK LA.A.1.1.2: The student identifies words and constructs meaning from text, illustrations, graphics, and charts using the strategies of phonics, word structure, and context clues.

52

Practice Book
Time Together • Lesson 6

© Harcourt

Name _____

▶ **Read the words in the box. Read the headings. Write each word in the correct group. Then add one more thing to each group.**

| apple | beet | letter | note | sandwich | story |

Things to Eat   **Things to Read**

_____   _____

- - - - - - - - - - - - - - - - -   - - - - - - - - - - - - - - - - -

_____   _____

_____   _____

- - - - - - - - - - - - - - - - -   - - - - - - - - - - - - - - - - -

_____   _____

_____   _____

- - - - - - - - - - - - - - - - -   - - - - - - - - - - - - - - - - -

_____   _____

- - - - - - - - - - - - - - - - -   - - - - - - - - - - - - - - - - -

_____   _____

FLORIDA BENCHMARK LA.A.1.1.3: The student uses knowledge of appropriate grade-, age-, and developmental-level vocabulary in reading.

53

Practice Book
Time Together • Lesson 6

Name _____

▶ **Read each clue. Write the words from the box where they belong in the puzzle.**

| down | brown | town | round | mound | found |

1. A baseball pitcher stands on this.
2. A color
3. The shape of a ball
4. A place with streets, houses, and shops
5. Up and _____
6. Lost and _____

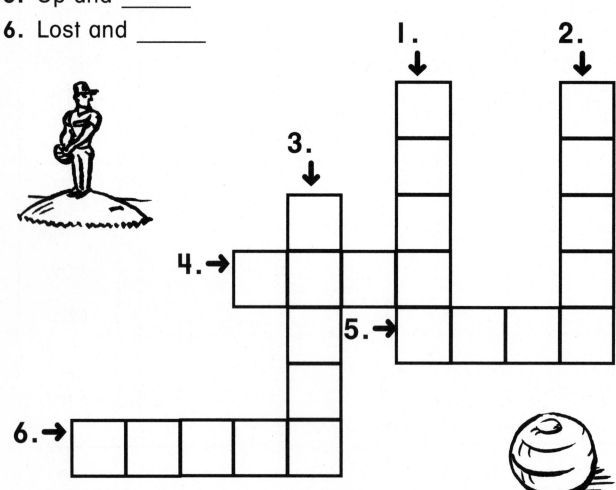

FLORIDA BENCHMARK LA.A.1.1.2: The student identifies words and constructs meaning from text, illustrations, graphics, and charts using the strategies of phonics, word structure, and context clues.

54

Practice Book
Time Together • Lesson 6

© Harcourt

▶ **Read the words. Then read the name of each group. Write each word in the group where it belongs.**

Words With Long i Spelled y

_____

_____

_____

_____

_____

Words With ou and ow

_____

_____

Other Words

_____

_____

_____

Spelling Words

my

fly

by

why

sky

try

out

now

any

eight

FLORIDA BENCHMARK LA.B.1.1.3: The student produces final simple documents that have been edited for correct spelling; appropriate end punctuation; correct capitalization of initial words, "I," and names of people; correct sentence structure; and correct usage of age-appropriate verb/subject and noun/pronoun agreement.

55

Name _____

▶ **Read the story. Write the word or words that best complete the sentence.**

| sky | cry | fly | Why | try | tie |

_____   _____

1. "_____ do you _____?"

Toad asked.

_____

2. "Because I can't _____ to my nest," said Owl.

_____

3. "I need to get into the _____, but I can't

_____

get my _____ out."

_____

4. "I will _____ to help,"

said Toad.

FLORIDA BENCHMARK LA.A.1.1.2: The student identifies words and
constructs meaning from text, illustrations, graphics, and charts
using the strategies of phonics, word structure, and context clues.

56

Practice Book
Time Together • Lesson 7

© Harcourt

▶ **Read the sentences. Each sentence tells how many. Circle the word that tells how many. Then color how many Teddy got.**

1. Teddy got three lamps.

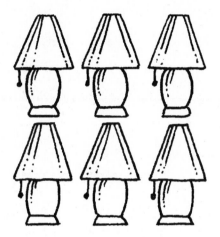

2. Teddy picked five buckets.

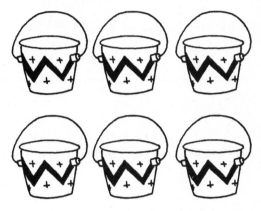

3. He got two plants.

4. He got one tent.

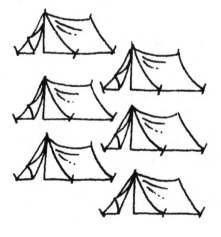

FLORIDA BENCHMARK LA.B.1.1.2: The student drafts and revises simple sentences and passages, stories, letters and simple explanations that express ideas clearly; show an awareness of topic and audience; have a beginning, middle, and ending; effectively use common words; have supporting detail; and are in legible printing.

► **Write the word from the box that best completes each sentence.**

pie	cry	by	lie	try

1. Toad and Owl sit _____ the fire.

2. "Let's eat some _____," says Toad.

3. Owl starts to _____.

4. "I can't tell a _____," says Owl.

   "I ate the pie!"

5. "Don't cry! I'll _____

   to cook some soup."

FLORIDA BENCHMARK LA.A.1.1.2: The student identifies words and constructs meaning from text, illustrations, graphics, and charts using the strategies of phonics, word structure, and context clues.

58

Practice Book
Time Together • Lesson 7

© Harcourt

Name _____

▶ **Write the word that best completes each sentence.**

again	blue	High	love	opened	Hello

_____

1. "_____, Betsy. It's me, Jill."

_____

2. "Hi Jill. Can you bring my _____ bag to school? I left it at your house again."

3. "OK," said Jill. "Did you know a new ice cream

_____

shop _____?"

_____

4. "No! I _____ ice cream! Where is it?"

_____

5. "It's on _____ Street. Let's go after school!"

FLORIDA BENCHMARK LA.A.1.1.3: The student uses knowledge of appropriate grade-, age-, and developmental-level vocabulary in reading.

59

Practice Book
Time Together • Lesson 7

© Harcourt

Name _____

▶ **Write a word from the box to complete each sentence.**

| fly | sandy | windy | sky | jelly |

1. The sun is out.

   _____
   - - - - - - - - - - - -

   The _____ is blue.

   _____
   - - - - - - - - - - - -

2. Birds _____ high above us.

   _____
   - - - - - - - - - - - -

3. It's getting pretty _____!

   _____
   - - - - - - - - - - - -

4. Gus wants his _____ sandwich.

   _____
   - - - - - - - - - - - -

5. We are all _____ when we leave.

FLORIDA BENCHMARK LA.A.1.1.2: The student identifies words and
constructs meaning from text, illustrations, graphics, and charts
using the strategies of phonics, word structure, and context clues.

60

Practice Book
Time Together • Lesson 7

© Harcourt

Name _____

▶ **Tess and Dan are at ABC Farm. The animals at this farm are in ABC order. Write the names of the animals Tess and Dan see as they walk through ABC Farm.**

frog	pig	horse
mouse	cow	duck

1. _____

2. _____

3. _____ 4. _____

5. _____

6. _____

© Harcourt

FLORIDA BENCHMARK LA.A.2.1.5: The student uses simple materials of the reference system to obtain information.

61

Practice Book
Time Together • Lesson 7

Name _____

▶ **Use a contraction to complete each sentence.**

| don't | can't | doesn't | Jack's | He's | He'll |

1. _____ making a garden.

2. _____ growing corn.

3. He _____ want animals to eat the plants.

4. _____ make a gate so they _____ get in.

5. The animals _____ like it!

FLORIDA BENCHMARK LA.A.1.1.2: The student identifies words and constructs meaning from text, illustrations, graphics, and charts using the strategies of phonics, word structure, and context clues.

62

Practice Book
Time Together • Lesson 7

© Harcourt

► **Read the words. Then read the name of each group. Write each word in the group where it belongs.**

Words With o-e

_____

_____

_____

_____

_____

_____

_____

_____

Words With y

_____

_____

_____

Words Without o or y

_____

_____

_____

Spelling Words

bone

cone

code

rode

rose

those

my

try

again

blue

FLORIDA BENCHMARK LA.B.1.1.3: The student produces final
simple documents that have been edited for correct spelling;
appropriate end punctuation; correct capitalization of initial words,
"I," and names of people; correct sentence structure; and correct
usage of age-appropriate verb/subject and noun/pronoun agreement.

63

Practice Book
Time Together • Lesson 8

▶ **Write the word that best completes
each sentence in the story.**

| home | nose | hole | stove | bone | mole |

_____

1. This is a _____ in the dirt.

_____

2. It is the door to my _____.

_____

3. You see, I am a _____.

_____

4. I sniff with my _____.

_____

5. I have a _____.

_____

6. I will make soup with this _____.

FLORIDA BENCHMARK LA.A.1.1.2: The student identifies words and
constructs meaning from text, illustrations, graphics, and charts
using the strategies of phonics, word structure, and context clues.

64

Practice Book
Time Together • Lesson 8

Name _____

▶ **Read the chart. Then write the word that best completes each sentence.**

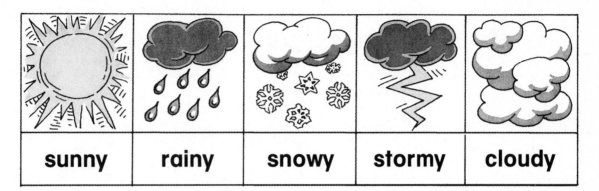

| sunny | rainy | snowy | stormy | cloudy |

1.  It is a _____ day.

_____

2.  It is a _____ day.

_____

3.  It is a _____ day.

_____

4. It is a _____ day.

TRY THIS Write a story about today's weather.

FLORIDA BENCHMARK LA.B.1.1.2: The student drafts and revises simple sentences and passages, stories, letters and simple explanations that express ideas clearly; show an awareness of topic and audience; have a beginning, middle, and ending; effectively use common words; have supporting detail; and are in legible printing.

Practice Book
Time Together • Lesson 8

Name _____

▶ **Read the words. Write the word that finishes each sentence.**

bone	home	pole	robe	woke

1. I am at _____.

2. My dog _____ me up.

3. That is why I am still in my _____.

4. He dug a hole for his _____.

5. Oh, no! He is digging by the flag _____!

FLORIDA BENCHMARK LA.A.1.1.2: The student identifies words and constructs meaning from text, illustrations, graphics, and charts using the strategies of phonics, word structure, and context clues.

66

Practice Book
Time Together • Lesson 8

Name _____

► **Write the word from the box that best completes each sentence.**

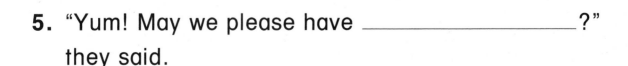

| another | wait | change | field | touch | wild | twelve |

_____

1. Pa Bear baked _____ apple pies.

_____

2. "Wait! Do not _____ the hot pies," he said.

3. Pa bear said, "No wild play in the house.

   Go be wild in the _____ ".

4. Then Pa said, "Now go _____ your shirts."

5. "Yum! May we please have _____?" they said.

FLORIDA BENCHMARK LA.A.1.1.3: The student uses knowledge of appropriate grade-, age-, and developmental-level vocabulary in reading.

 67

Practice Book
Time Together • Lesson 8

© Harcourt

Name _____

▶ **Write the words from the box where they belong in the puzzle.**

| cot | box | nose | note | rose | sob |

1. a flower
2. something you write
3. part of your face
4. cry
5. a small bed
6. you can put things in this

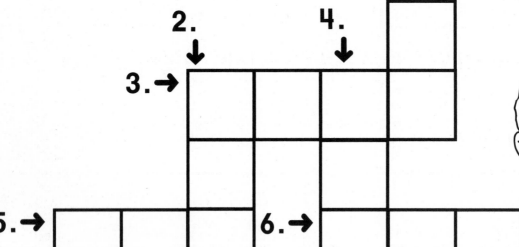

FLORIDA BENCHMARK LA.A.1.1.2: The student identifies words and constructs meaning from text, illustrations, graphics, and charts using the strategies of phonics, word structure, and context clues.

Practice Book
Time Together • Lesson 8

© Harcourt

Name _____

▶ **Read each sentence. Write <u>cl</u>, <u>gl</u>, or <u>sl</u> to finish each word.**

_____

1. The _____own drinks a glass of milk.

_____

2. He is a _____eepy clown.

_____

3. He is _____ad it is time for bed.

_____   _____

4. He _____ips on his _____ippers.

_____

5. He _____imbs into bed

_____

and goes to _____eep.

FLORIDA BENCHMARK LA.A.1.1.2: The student identifies words and constructs meaning from text, illustrations, graphics, and charts using the strategies of phonics, word structure, and context clues.

69

Practice Book
Time Together • Lesson 8

© Harcourt

Patch's Treat

1

This cat will do anything for fun!
Those feet look like socks.

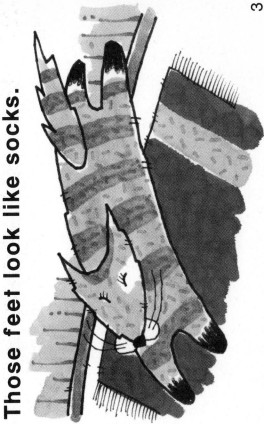

3

Fold

© Harcourt

Fold

Let's go home, Patch. You need
a treat. I'll feed you.

8

Please, Dad, can I keep him?
I'll also clean my room for him.

6

71

4

There is only one cat left.
He has a patch on his eye.

2

Jean can't keep her cats.
She needs to find good homes
for them.

Fold

© Harcourt

Fold

5

Please, can I keep him?
I'll write to Jean and tell
her how he is.

7

What should we call him?
I know! We can call him
Patch!

1

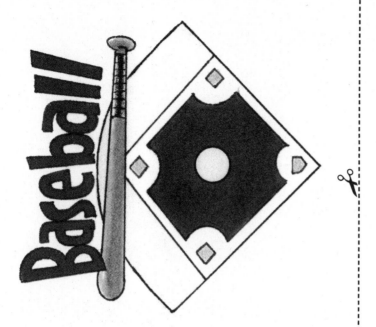

3

Fold

© Harcourt

Fold

8

People like
to watch the
players step
up to the plate
and hit the ball.
CRACK!

Children in many
countries play the game.
They play in the same way—
6 with a ball, a bat, and a mitt.

2

Baseball is played all over the world. It doesn't take much to play the game. You need a ball, a bat, some mitts, and a big place to play.

4

The game was first played in the United States of America. It was called "town ball." Later it became baseball.

5

7

Eating Yummy Cake

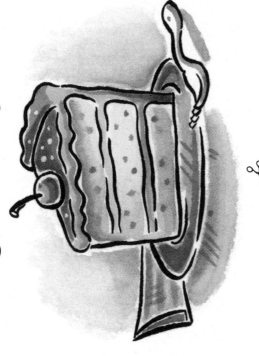

— Fold —

I would like a different kind of cake. Do you have Sticky Cake?

— Fold —

I had this when I was four years old! Patty Cake is the best!

8

Hold on. I have a cake that is still warm from the oven.

6

Would you like water
with your tea and
cake?

4

Sticky Cake?
I haven't had
Sticky Cake in years.

Fold

Fold

Have some Patty Cake.
Please tell me how you like it. 7

Too bad. Do you have
Happy Cake? Or
Hungry Cake?

5

One More Time

1

One likes to cook dinner.

3

© Harcourt

Four white birds smile and think
of their friend and his fine tales.

8

One bird wants to fly for
miles and miles.

9

Five white birds share the same nest. They are together most of the time.

One bird tells tales from when he was young.

Fold

Fold

Why will this bird fly away? He'll go because he wants to see it one more time.

7

The others sit in front of him and listen. They smile and hide their beaks.

5

How to Make a Face

Fold

© Harcourt

3

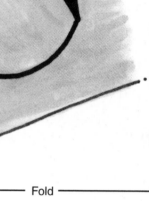

Always start with a nice, big circle.

Fold

8

Now you make a face.

You're almost finished. Does it look pretty? You can make it fancy or simple.

9

2

First, use a pencil.

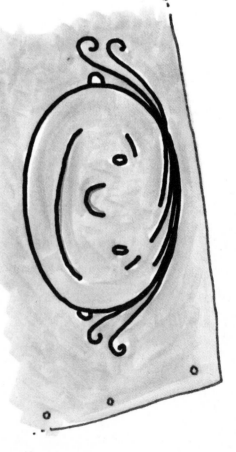

4

Make a big curve in the center. Do this once.

5

Add two circles for eyes. Make them even.

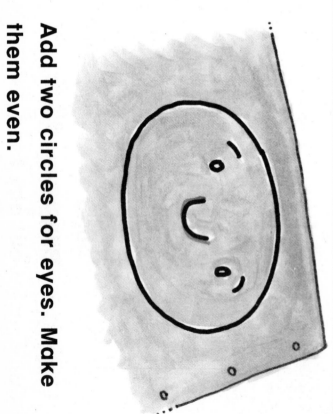

7

Say, don't forget the smile!

Fold

Fold

1

Billy Brown's Lunch

Fold

© Harcourt

3

He took the list to town.

Fold

Billy Brown took care of the food. He set out flowers. The

8 friends ate lunch.

They went around town, buying things from Billy's list. They

6 didn't leave out any food.

81

2

Billy Brown made a
list of things to buy.

4

In town, he met a friend. "Are
you busy?" he asked.

"I'm free until eight," she said.

Fold

© Harcourt

Fold

"How about lunch at my house?"
said Billy.

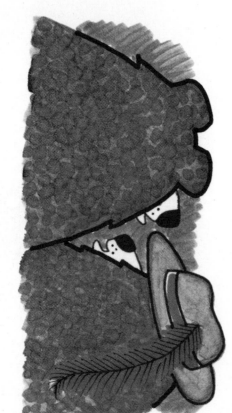

5

7

1

A Dream to Fly

— Fold —

© Harcourt

3

"Some day I'll go up in the sky. I want to try."

— Fold —

Up in the sky, you will see Mike fly, again and again.

8

Well, Mike got his wish. He got in a plane.

6

2

Mike had a dream.
He wanted to fly.

4

Mike went to school. He wasn't shy. He opened the doors.

"Hello from up here!
It's as easy as pie!"

7

"I'm going to fly. It's my dream to be up in the sky."

5

© Harcourt

Hello, Neighbor • Cut-out Fold-up Book   **84**

Squirrels at Home

1

— Fold —

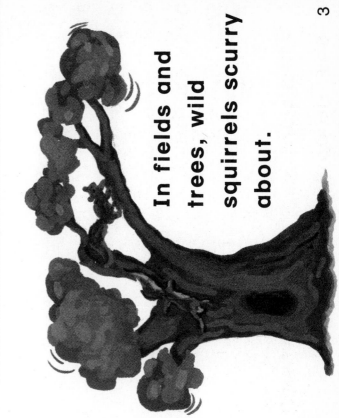

In fields and trees, wild squirrels scurry about.

3

— Fold —

Those squirrels are busy twelve months a year!

8

Squirrels quickly run up trees and poles. They can leap from branch to branch.

6

4

At the change of
seasons, squirrels
dig holes to store
food. They are
busy as they
wait for winter.

2

Squirrels are found
all over the world.

Fold

© Harcourt

5

7

One squirrel doesn't want
another to touch its food.

Fold

• TROPHIES •

Level Five

Gather Around

► **Read the words. Then read the name of each group. Write each word in the group where it belongs.**

Words That End With <u>igh</u>	Words That End With <u>ight</u>
_____	_____
_____	_____
_____	_____
	_____
Words Without <u>i</u>	_____
_____	_____
_____	_____
_____	_____
_____	_____
_____	_____
_____	

Spelling Words

high
night
light
right
might
bright
rode
those
touch
twelve

FLORIDA BENCHMARK LA.B.1.1.3: The student produces final simple documents that have been edited for correct spelling; appropriate end punctuation; correct capitalization of initial words, "I," and names of people; correct sentence structure; and correct usage of age-appropriate verb/subject and noun/pronoun agreement.

2

Practice Book
Gather Around • Lesson 1

© Harcourt

Name _____

▶ **Circle the pictures whose names have the /ī/ sound. Then write the names of the pictures you circled.**

high	fright	night	sigh	light

1.

_____

- - - - - - - - - - - - - -

_____

2.

_____

- - - - - - - - - - - - - -

_____

3.

_____

- - - - - - - - - - - - - -

_____

4.

_____

- - - - - - - - - - - - - -

_____

5.

_____

- - - - - - - - - - - - - -

_____

6.

_____

- - - - - - - - - - - - - -

_____

© Harcourt

FLORIDA BENCHMARK LA.A.1.1.2: The student identifies words and constructs meaning from text, illustrations, graphics, and charts using the strategies of phonics, word structure, and context clues.

3

Practice Book
Gather Around • Lesson 1

► **Add <u>er</u> or <u>est</u> to the word so that it correctly completes the sentence. Then write the word.**

bright

_____

- - - - - - - - - - - - - - - - - - - -

1. This bird has _____

colors than that bird.

---

high

_____

- - - - - - - - - - - - - - - - - - - -

2. The blue bird lands on a _____

branch than the green bird.

---

tight

_____

- - - - - - - - - - - - - - - - - - - -

3. Birds make nests in the _____

places.

TRY THIS With a partner, act out the words <u>light</u>, <u>lighter</u>, <u>lightest</u> and <u>high</u>, <u>higher</u>, <u>highest</u>.

FLORIDA BENCHMARK LA.A.1.1.3: The student uses knowledge of appropriate grade-, age-, and developmental-level vocabulary in reading.

4

Practice Book
Gather Around • Lesson 1

▶ **The letters <u>igh</u> stand for the /ī/ sound.**
Circle the words that have the /ī/ sound.

1. branch

2. light

3. night

4. high

5. fright

6. nest

TRY THIS Write another word that rhymes with <u>sight</u>. Draw a picture for it. Then write a sentence using the word.

FLORIDA BENCHMARK LA.A.1.1.2: The student identifies words and constructs meaning from text, illustrations, graphics, and charts using the strategies of phonics, word structure, and context clues.

5

Practice Book
Gather Around • Lesson 1

Name _____

▶ **Read the words in the box. Write the
word that best completes each sentence.**

| afraid | flew | learn | nothing | thought | wonder |

1. Bob _____ off to join his friends.

2. He will _____ a lot out there.

3. I _____ where he is now.

4. I _____ he would be back by now.

5. Don't be _____.
Bob will come back.

FLORIDA BENCHMARK LA.A.1.1.3: The student uses knowledge of
appropriate grade-, age-, and developmental-level vocabulary in
reading.

6

Practice Book
Gather Around • Lesson 1

© Harcourt

▶ **Write the word from the box that names each picture.**

| feet | light | coat | night | seal | sigh |

1.

_____
- - - - - - - - - - - - - - -
_____

2.

_____
- - - - - - - - - - - - - - -
_____

3.

_____
- - - - - - - - - - - - - - -
_____

4.

_____
- - - - - - - - - - - - - - -
_____

5.

ahhh!

_____
- - - - - - - - - - - - - - -
_____

6.

_____
- - - - - - - - - - - - - - -
_____

FLORIDA BENCHMARK LA.A.1.1.2: The student identifies words and constructs meaning from text, illustrations, graphics, and charts using the strategies of phonics, word structure, and context clues.

7

Practice Book
Gather Around • Lesson 1

Name _____

▶ **Read the story. Then read each pair of
sentences. Circle the sentence that tells
what happened in the story.**

"Where is my kitten? Have you
seen my kitten?" asked Kip.

"No," said Mom. "Go and look."

So Kip went out to look for his
kitten. He looked up in the tree. He
looked under the bush and by the
rocks. He saw some birds and bugs.
He did not see his kitten.

Kip felt sad. He walked back to
his door. There was his kitten,
sitting on the mat!

I. Kip went out to look at the birds.
   Kip went out to look for his kitten.

2. Kip looked under the bush.
   Kip looked up in the sky.

3. Kip opened the door.
   Kip was sad until he saw his kitten.

FLORIDA BENCHMARK LA.E.1.1.2: The student identifies the story
elements of setting, plot, character, problem, and solution/resolution.

▲ 8

Practice Book
Gather Around • Lesson 1

© Harcourt

▶ **Read the word above each line. Add ed or ing to the word to complete the sentence. Remember to drop the final e.**

like
_____

- - - - - - - - - - - - - - - - - -

1. I have always _____ spring.

_____

rake
_____

- - - - - - - - - - - - - - - - - -

2. My dad is _____ the fall leaves.

_____

chase
_____

- - - - - - - - - - - - - - - - - -

3. I do not like _____ snowflakes.

_____

make
_____

- - - - - - - - - - - - - - - - - -

4. Are you _____ a snowman?

_____

bake
_____

- - - - - - - - - - - - - - - - - -

5. We _____ a cake.

FLORIDA BENCHMARK LA.A.1.1.2: The student identifies words and constructs meaning from text, illustrations, graphics, and charts using the strategies of phonics, word structure, and context clues.

9

Practice Book
Gather Around • Lesson 1

Name _____

▶ **Read the words. Then read the name of
each group. Write each word in the group
where it belongs.**

Words With <u>ay</u>

_____ _____

_____ _____

_____ _____

Words With <u>ai</u>

_____ _____

_____ _____

Words Without Long <u>a</u>

_____ _____

_____ _____

_____ _____

Spelling Words

day

say

sail

pail

pay

play

right

high

learn

join

© Harcourt

FLORIDA BENCHMARK LA.B.1.1.3: The student produces final
simple documents that have been edited for correct spelling;
appropriate end punctuation; correct capitalization of initial words,
"I," and names of people; correct sentence structure; and correct
usage of age-appropriate verb/subject and noun/pronoun agreement.

10

▶ **Circle the word that names the picture.**
Then write the word.

1.

hat   hot   hay

_____

- - - - - - - - - - - - - - -

_____

2.

pan   play   paint

_____

- - - - - - - - - - - - - - -

_____

3.

rain   ride   rail

_____

- - - - - - - - - - - - - - -

_____

4.

snack   sail   snail

_____

- - - - - - - - - - - - - - -

_____

5.

tray   tail   trap

_____

- - - - - - - - - - - - - - -

_____

6.

tree   tired   train

_____

- - - - - - - - - - - - - - -

_____

TRY THIS Write a word that rhymes with <u>hay</u> and has <u>ay</u>. Write a word that rhymes with <u>snail</u> and has <u>ai</u>. Draw a picture for each word.

FLORIDA BENCHMARK LA.A.1.1.2: The student identifies words and constructs meaning from text, illustrations, graphics, and charts using the strategies of phonics, word structure, and context clues.

11

Practice Book
Gather Around • Lesson 2

Name _____

▶ **Look at the picture. Write a verb to complete each sentence.**

play	stay	wait	mail

_____

1. Frog wanted Toad to _____ ball.

_____

2. Toad wanted to _____ a letter first.

_____

3. Frog said, "I will sit and _____ for you."

_____

4. Toad asked Frog to _____ for supper.

TRY THIS Work with a partner. Make a list of as many verbs as you can.

FLORIDA BENCHMARK LA.D.1.1.1: The student recognizes basic patterns in and functions of language (patterns such as characteristic sounds and rhythms and those found in written forms; functions such as asking questions, expressing oneself, describing objects or experiences, and explaining).

12

Practice Book
Gather Around • Lesson 2

© Harcourt

Name _____

► **Write the word from the box that best completes each sentence.**

play	stay	day	rain	wait

_____

1. I do not like the _____.

_____

2. I can't _____ outside.

_____

3. I don't want to _____ home.

_____

4. I want a sunny _____.

_____

5. I will _____

for the sun to come out.

TRY THIS Use the words <u>mail</u>, <u>day</u>, and <u>gray</u> to write a short poem or story about the weather.

FLORIDA BENCHMARK LA.A.1.1.2: The student identifies words and constructs meaning from text, illustrations, graphics, and charts using the strategies of phonics, word structure, and context clues.

13

Practice Book
Gather Around • Lesson 2

© Harcourt

Name _____

▶ **Read the words in the box. Write the word that best completes each sentence.**

| caught | cold | hurried | near | son | sure |

_____

1. Mr. Bates took his _____ fishing.

_____

2. They went to a lake _____ their house.

_____

3. The day was _____
and wet, but they had fun.

_____

5. "Look at what I _____," said his son.

_____

6. They _____
home with the big fish.

FLORIDA BENCHMARK LA.A.1.1.3: The student uses knowledge of appropriate grade-, age-, and developmental-level vocabulary in reading.

14

Practice Book
Gather Around • Lesson 2

© Harcourt

Name _____

▶ **Write the words where they belong in the puzzle.**

| gate | lake | nail | rain | hay | rake |

1.

2.

3.

4.

5.

6.

1. ↓

2. →

4. ↓

3. →

5. →

6. ↓

FLORIDA BENCHMARK LA.A.1.1.2: The student identifies words and constructs meaning from text, illustrations, graphics, and charts using the strategies of phonics, word structure, and context clues.

15

Practice Book
Gather Around • Lesson 2

Name _____

▶ **Add the endings <u>ed</u> and <u>ing</u> to each word. Remember to drop the final <u>e</u>.**

	ed	**ing**
1. close		
2. scare		
3. snore		

▶ **Write the correct word from the chart to finish each sentence.**

1. Why am I _____ this door?

2. The pig is _____ in his sleep.

FLORIDA BENCHMARK LA.A.1.1.2: The student identifies words and constructs meaning from text, illustrations, graphics, and charts using the strategies of phonics, word structure, and context clues.

16

Practice Book
Gather Around • Lesson 2

▶ **Read the words. Then read the name of each group. Write each word in the group where it belongs.**

Words With <u>ind</u>	Words With <u>ild</u>
_____	_____
_____	_____
_____	_____
_____	_____

Words Without <u>i</u>

_____   _____

_____   _____

_____   _____

Spelling Words

find

kind

mind

mild

child

wild

day

play

sure

son

FLORIDA BENCHMARK LA.B.1.1.3: The student produces final simple documents that have been edited for correct spelling; appropriate end punctuation; correct capitalization of initial words, "I," and names of people; correct sentence structure; and correct usage of age-appropriate verb/subject and noun/pronoun agreement.

17

Practice Book
Gather Around • Lesson 3

▶ **Choose a word in the box that rhymes with each underlined word and makes sense. Write it on the line.**

find	behind	wild

1. Do you <u>mind</u>? There's a big

_____

- - - - - - - - - - - - - - -

frog _____ us.

2. At the zoo, a <u>child</u> saw these words:

_____

- - - - - - - - - - - - - - -

"Do not feed our _____

animals."

3. You need to <u>wind</u> this toy.

_____

- - - - - - - - - - - - - - -

The baby will _____

it and play with it.

TRY THIS Make your own pair of sentences with two words from the box or other words that rhyme with them.

© Harcourt

FLORIDA BENCHMARK LA.A.1.1.2: The student identifies words and constructs meaning from text, illustrations, graphics, and charts using the strategies of phonics, word structure, and context clues.

18

Practice Book
Gather Around • Lesson 3

Name _____

▶ **Write the verb that best completes each sentence.**

drink	find	help	make	fill

_____
- - - - - - - - - - - -

1. I _____ the bird bath.

_____
- - - - - - - - - - -

2. Birds _____ from it.

_____
- - - - - - - - - - -

3. They come and _____ seeds in our feeder.

_____
- - - - - - - - -

4. We _____ birds because we like them.

_____
- - - - - - - - -

5. I _____ bird feeders for my friends, too.

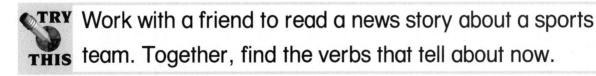

TRY THIS Work with a friend to read a news story about a sports team. Together, find the verbs that tell about now.

FLORIDA BENCHMARK LA.D.1.1.1: The student recognizes basic patterns in and functions of language (patterns such as characteristic sounds and rhythms and those found in written forms; functions such as asking questions, expressing oneself, describing objects or experiences, and explaining).

19

© Harcourt

Name _____

▶ **Write the word from the box that best completes each sentence.**

find	behind	wild	blind	mind

1. It can see.

_____

It is not _____.

2. It is not tame.

_____

It is _____.

3. It is not lost.

_____

I can _____ it.

4. A tadpole's tail is not in front.

_____

It is _____.

5. A tadpole doesn't think like we do.

_____

It has a _____ of its own.

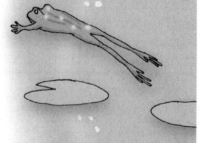

FLORIDA BENCHMARK LA.A.1.1.2: The student identifies words and constructs meaning from text, illustrations, graphics, and charts using the strategies of phonics, word structure, and context clues.

20

Practice Book
Gather Around • Lesson 3

© Harcourt

Name _____

▶ **Circle the word that best completes each sentence. Then write the word.**

both
during
ready

_____
- - - - - - - - - - - - - - -

1. Are _____ bears sleeping?

---

both
during
ready

_____
- - - - - - - - - - - - - - -

2. Yes, they sleep _____ the winter.

---

both
during
ready

_____
- - - - - - - - - - - - - - -

3. In spring they are _____ to wake up.

---

both
during
ready

_____
- - - - - - - - - - - - - - -

4. Then they will _____ catch fish.

---

both
during
ready

_____
- - - - - - - - - - - - - - -

5. They will be _____ to eat.

© Harcourt

FLORIDA BENCHMARK LA.A.1.1.3: The student uses knowledge of appropriate grade-, age-, and developmental-level vocabulary in reading.

21

Practice Book
Gather Around • Lesson 3

Name _____

▶ **Write the word from the box that best completes each sentence.**

hide	child	kite	like	wild

_____

1. Who is that _____?

_____

_____

2. She will _____ by that big tree.

_____

_____

3. She has a great _____.

_____

_____

4. The wind is _____ today.

_____

_____

5. We all _____ kites.

FLORIDA BENCHMARK LA.A.1.1.2: The student identifies words and constructs meaning from text, illustrations, graphics, and charts using the strategies of phonics, word structure, and context clues.

22

Practice Book
Gather Around • Lesson 3

© Harcourt

▶ **Read the paragraph. Write the main idea in the box. Write the details in the circles.**

Ducks are born knowing many things. Ducklings know that they must follow their mother. Ducklings also know how to swim. The mother does not have to show them.

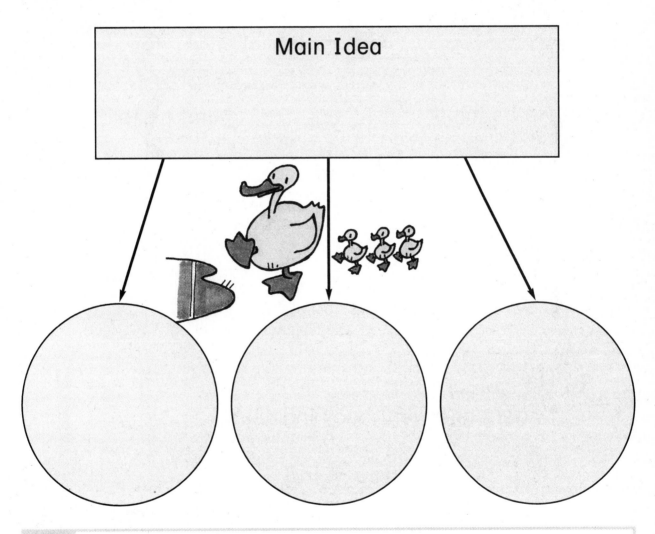

Main Idea

TRY THIS Think of a pet or other animal you know. Find out what things that animal knows when it is born. Find out what things the animal has to learn.

FLORIDA BENCHMARK LA.A.2.1.1: The student determines the main idea or essential message from text and identifies supporting information.

23

Practice Book
Gather Around • Lesson 3

Name _____

▶ **Look at the words and endings. Write the word that completes the sentence. Double the last letter before you add <u>ed</u> or <u>ing</u>.**

step + ed
_____

1. Marco _____ outside.

slip + ing
_____

2. He began _____ and he fell!

stop + ed
_____

3. Marco _____ to think.

snap + ed
_____

4. He _____ his
fingers and went back inside.

step + ing
_____

5. Marco is _____ into
his skates.

FLORIDA BENCHMARK LA.A.1.1.2: The student identifies words and constructs meaning from text, illustrations, graphics, and charts using the strategies of phonics, word structure, and context clues.

24

Practice Book
Gather Around • Lesson 3

© Harcourt

▶ **Read the words. Then read the name of each group. Write each word in the group where it belongs.**

Words With <u>old</u>	**Other Words With <u>o</u>**
_____	_____
_____	_____
_____	_____
_____	_____
_____	_____
_____	_____

Words Without <u>o</u>

_____	_____
_____	_____
_____	_____

Spelling Words

old
fold
told
cold
roll
most
find
child
both
during

FLORIDA BENCHMARK LA.B.1.1.3: The student produces final simple documents that have been edited for correct spelling; appropriate end punctuation; correct capitalization of initial words, "I," and names of people; correct sentence structure; and correct usage of age-appropriate verb/subject and noun/pronoun agreement.

Practice Book
Gather Around • Lesson 4

▶ **Read the numbered clues. Use the words from the box to complete the puzzle.**

hello	gold	no	also
ago	cold	soda	go

Across

2. a long time ___

3. ____ pop

4. stop and __

6. _____, how are you?

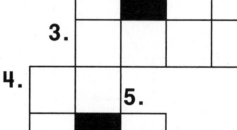

Down

1. icy ____

2. me ____ (too)

4. silver and ____

5. __, thanks

© Harcourt

Name _____

▶ **Write <u>am</u>, <u>is</u>, or <u>are</u> to finish each sentence.**

_____
- - - - - - - - - - - - -

1. What _____ you doing?

_____
- - - - - - - - - - - - -

2. I _____ playing with a yo-yo.

_____
- - - - - - - - - - - - -

3. _____ you good at it?

_____
- - - - - - - - - - - - -

4. My sister _____ better.

_____
- - - - - - - - - - - - -

5. She _____ standing over there.

_____
- - - - - - - - - - - - -

6. I _____ taking lessons from her.

 TRY THIS   Work with a partner to answer the question "What are you doing?" Answer two ways—beginning with "I am" and with "We are."

FLORIDA BENCHMARK LA.D.1.1.1: The student recognizes basic patterns in and functions of language (patterns such as characteristic sounds and rhythms and those found in written forms; functions such as asking questions, expressing oneself, describing objects or experiences, and explaining).

27

Practice Book
Gather Around • Lesson 4

Name _____

▶ **Choose the word that best completes each sentence. Then write the word.**

fold   old   told

_____

- - - - - - - - - - -

1. Mr. Rabbit broke his _____ bed.

---

go   so   got

_____

- - - - - - - - - - -

2. Mr. and Mrs. Rabbit _____ get a new bed.

---

soda   spot   sofa

_____

- - - - - - - - - - -

3. Mr. Rabbit sees a nice _____ bed.

Old   Sold   Socks

_____

- - - - - - - - - - -

4. Mr. and Mrs. Rabbit say, "_____!"

 TRY THIS Make up rhyming sentences using the words <u>sold</u>, <u>old</u>, and <u>told</u>. Say your sentences to classmates.

FLORIDA BENCHMARK LA.A.1.1.2: The student identifies words and constructs meaning from text, illustrations, graphics, and charts using the strategies of phonics, word structure, and context clues.

28

Practice Book
Gather Around • Lesson 4

Name _____

▶ **Read the words in the box. Write the word that best completes each sentence.**

| clues | detective | floor | nature | piece | pulls |

_____

1. I like to watch what happens in _____.

_____

2. The bird _____ up a bit of yarn.

_____

3. Now it has a little _____ of cloth.

_____

4. These are _____ to what the bird is doing.

_____

5. It is making the _____ of its nest soft.

FLORIDA BENCHMARK LA.A.1.1.2: The student identifies words and
constructs meaning from text, illustrations, graphics, and charts
using the strategies of phonics, word structure, and context clues.

29

Practice Book
Gather Around • Lesson 4

© Harcourt

Name _____

▶ **Circle the sentence that tells about each picture.**

1. "Let's go!" said the colt.

   "No!" said the girl.

   "Hello!" said the ant.

2. A pig thinks he is cold.

   A pig thinks he has lost his gold.

   A pig thinks he has lost his bone.

3. I am going home now.

   I am over on the sofa.

   I am holding the gold in this safe.

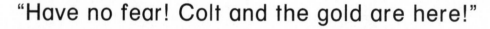

4. I have a total of 3 bags.

   I have a total of 3 ropes.

   I have a total of 3 bones.

5. "Have no fear! Cold soda is here!"

   "Have no fear! Your roses are here!"

   "Have no fear! Colt and the gold are here!"

6. The pig holds his gold.

   The colt keeps the gold.

   The colt calls the pig.

FLORIDA BENCHMARK LA.A.1.1.2: The student identifies words and constructs meaning from text, illustrations, graphics, and charts using the strategies of phonics, word structure, and context clues.

30

Practice Book
Gather Around • Lesson 4

© Harcourt

Name _____

▶ **Read the selection. Find the sentence that tells the main idea. Write it on the lines. Then write a title for the selection.**

Title

_____

- -

_____

Much more than water is in the sea. The sea is filled with living things. Many animals and plants live there. Some of the animals look like plants. We use many of the living things that are in the sea.

Main Idea

_____

- -

_____

- -

_____

- -

_____

© Harcourt

FLORIDA BENCHMARK LA.A.2.1.5: The student uses simple materials of the reference system to obtain information.

 31

Practice Book
Gather Around • Lesson 4

Name _____

▶ Finish each sentence. Write the contraction for the two words above it.

| They've | You've | You'd | We'd | We're |

We are

_____

- - - - - - - - - -

1. _____ in our new bed.

We would

_____

- - - - - - - - - -

2. _____ love you to come see.

You have

_____

- - - - - - - - - -

3. _____ been here before.

They have

_____

- - - - - - - - - -

4. _____ got their own bed.

 TRY THIS Make a list of things you would like. Begin each item on your list with the words <u>I'd like</u>.

FLORIDA BENCHMARK LA.A.1.1.2: The student identifies words and constructs meaning from text, illustrations, graphics, and charts using the strategies of phonics, word structure, and context clues.

32

Practice Book
Gather Around • Lesson 4

© Harcourt

▶ **Read the words. Then read the name of each group. Write each word in the group where it belongs.**

Words That End With <u>age</u>	Words That End With <u>dge</u>
_____	_____
_____	_____
_____	_____
_____	_____

Words Without <u>g</u>

_____	_____
_____	_____
_____	_____

Spelling Words

age
page
cage
badge
budge
fudge
old
most
floor
piece

FLORIDA BENCHMARK LA.B.1.1.3: The student produces final simple documents that have been edited for correct spelling; appropriate end punctuation; correct capitalization of initial words, "I," and names of people; correct sentence structure; and correct usage of age-appropriate verb/subject and noun/pronoun agreement.

33

Practice Book
Gather Around • Lesson 5

Name _____

▶ **Write the word from the box that best completes each sentence.**

large	age	bridge	edge

_____

- - - - - - - - - - - - - - - - - - - -

1. I came to a _____ puddle.

2. A big animal sat by the

_____

- - - - - - - - - - - - - - - - - - - -

_____ of the puddle.

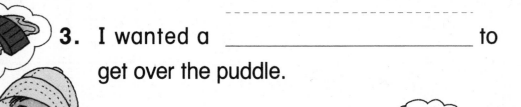

_____

- - - - - - - - - - - - - - - - - - - -

3. I wanted a _____ to
   get over the puddle.

_____

- - - - - - - - - - - - - - - - - - - -

4. Kids my _____
   like puddles.

 TRY THIS Make a chart about the ages of your classmates.
Give your chart a title that uses the word <u>age</u>.

FLORIDA BENCHMARK LA.A.1.1.2: The student identifies words and constructs meaning from text, illustrations, graphics, and charts using the strategies of phonics, word structure, and context clues.

34

Practice Book
Gather Around • Lesson 5

© Harcourt

Name _____

▶ **Write the word that best completes each sentence.**

| spilled | filled | needed | cleaned |

_____

_ _ _ _ _ _ _ _ _ _ _ _ _ _ _

1. Lenny _____ to make some ice.

_____

_ _ _ _ _ _ _ _ _ _ _ _ _ _ _

2. He _____ the ice tray with water.

_____

_ _ _ _ _ _ _ _ _ _ _ _ _ _ _

3. The water _____ all over.

_____

_ _ _ _ _ _ _ _ _ _ _ _ _ _ _

4. Lenny _____ up

the mess.

 TRY THIS With a partner, take turns reading the sentences and acting them out.

FLORIDA BENCHMARK LA.D.1.1.1: The student recognizes basic patterns in and functions of language (patterns such as characteristic sounds and rhythms and those found in written forms; functions such as asking questions, expressing oneself, describing objects or experiences, and explaining).

△35

© Harcourt

Name _____

▶ **Look at the picture. Then do what the sentences tell you to do.**

1. Make the pig on stage pink.

2. Give the pig a huge hat.

3. Find the largest bed. Put a badge on it.

4. Draw a huge pillow on one edge of a bed.

5. Find the cage next to the largest bed. Draw a pet gerbil inside the cage.

6. A large crowd is watching from the bridge. Draw a ring around the large crowd.

 TRY THIS Write a sentence about this picture. Use some of the words from the sentences on the page.

FLORIDA BENCHMARK LA.A.1.1.2: The student identifies words and constructs meaning from text, illustrations, graphics, and charts using the strategies of phonics, word structure, and context clues. **36**

Practice Book
Gather Around • Lesson 5

© Harcourt

Name _____

▶ **Write the word from the box that best completes each sentence.**

angry	nearly	okay	sorry

1.

I hope you are

_____

– – – – – – – – – – – –

_____ .

2.

_____

– – – – – – – – – – – –

I _____

fell down.

3.

_____

– – – – – – – – – – – –

I'm _____

I bumped into you.

4.

I hope you are not

_____

– – – – – – – – – – – –

_____ !

FLORIDA BENCHMARK LA.A.1.1.3: The student uses knowledge of appropriate grade-, age-, and developmental-level vocabulary in reading.

© Harcourt

Name _____

► **Circle the word that names each picture.
Then write the word.**

1.

cap   cape   cage

_____

- - - - - - - - - - - -

_____

2.

rice   rose   race

_____

- - - - - - - - - - - -

_____

3.

jug   judge   jam

_____

- - - - - - - - - - - -

_____

4.

lass   lace   lap

_____

- - - - - - - - - - - -

_____

5.

fact   face   film

_____

- - - - - - - - - - - -

_____

6.

page   peg   pass

_____

- - - - - - - - - - - -

_____

FLORIDA BENCHMARK LA.A.1.1.2: The student identifies words and
constructs meaning from text, illustrations, graphics, and charts
using the strategies of phonics, word structure, and context clues.

Practice Book
Gather Around • Lesson 5

© Harcourt

Name _____ _____

▶ **Read the story. Then complete the sentences.**

"Will you take me to the lake, Mom?" asked Jen.

"No. I have to work," said Mom.

"Will you take me to the lake, Dad?" asked Jen.

"No. I have lots to do," said Dad.

Just then, Gram called. "Hi, Gram," said Jen.

"Will you take me to the lake?"

"That's why I called you, Jen. I want to take you to the lake," said Gram.

"Oh good! Thank you Gram," said Jen.

_____
----

1. Jen wanted to go to _____.

_____
----

2. _____ said no.

_____
----

3. _____ said no, too.

_____
----

4. _____ said she would take Jen.

FLORIDA BENCHMARK LA.E.1.1.2: The student identifies the story elements of setting, plot, character, problem, and solution/resolution.

39

Practice Book
Gather Around • Lesson 5

© Harcourt

Name _____

▶ Write the contraction from the bo____ for
the two words above each senter____e.

| I'd | We're | We'd | You're | I've |

We are
_____

1. _____ going to play a game.

I would
_____

2. _____ like to play, too.

We would
_____

3. _____ like to have you on our team.

I have
_____

4. _____ never played this game.

You are
_____

5. _____ going to like it!

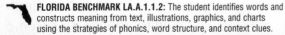
FLORIDA BENCHMARK LA.A.1.1.2: The student identifies words and
constructs meaning from text, illustrations, graphics, and charts
using the strategies of phonics, word structure, and context clues.
40

Practice Book
Gather Around • Lesson 5

© Harcourt

► **Read the words. Then read the name of each group. Write each word in the group where it belongs.**

Words With Silent <u>e</u>

_____   _____

_____   _____

_____   _____

_____   _____

_____   _____

_____   _____

Words With <u>y</u>

_____   _____

_____   _____

Spelling Words

tube
cube
cute
use
rule
huge
page
fudge
angry
sorry

FLORIDA BENCHMARK LA.B.1.1.3: The student produces final simple documents that have been edited for correct spelling; appropriate end punctuation; correct capitalization of initial words, "I," and names of people; correct sentence structure; and correct usage of age-appropriate verb/subject and noun/pronoun agreement.

41

Practice Book
Gather Around • Lesson 6

▶ **Circle the word that best completes each sentence. Then write the word.**

1. The cat looked up and said, "It is

    _____

    -

    _____!"

    hand
    huge
    tube

2. _____

    -

    "It smells like _____,"
    said the mule.

    perfume
    cute
    perform

3. The cat sniffed but could not smell

    _____

    -

    the _____.

    purple
    perfume
    huge

4. _____

    -

    "_____ me, but it has
    no smell," said the cat.

    Every
    Excuse
    Cube

5. _____

    -

    "Oh! _____ me!" said
    the mule. "I was sniffing a flower."

    Empty
    Plume
    Excuse

FLORIDA BENCHMARK LA.A.1.1.2: The student identifies words and
constructs meaning from text, illustrations, graphics, and charts
using the strategies of phonics, word structure, and context clues.

42

Practice Book
Gather Around • Lesson 6

© Harcourt

Name _____

▶ Write <u>was</u> or <u>were</u> to complete each sentence. Then circle <u>one</u> or <u>more than one</u> to show how many people or things the action word tells about.

1. I _____ skating all day.

    one

    more than one

2. They _____ skating, too.

    one

    more than one

3. We _____ in a pile!

    one

    more than one

4. We _____ all okay.

    one

    more than one

TRY THIS With a classmate, tell about three things that happened yesterday. Use <u>was</u> and <u>were</u> in your discussion.

FLORIDA BENCHMARK LA.D.1.1.1: The student recognizes basic patterns in and functions of language (patterns such as characteristic sounds and rhythms and those found in written forms; functions such as asking questions, expressing oneself, describing objects or experiences, and explaining).

Name _____

▶ **Write words from the box to complete the story.**

cube	huge	Use	cute

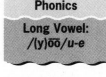

"I am never coming out," sniffled Mole. "I am small,

_____

but I want to be _____. I want my den to be

_____

shaped like a _____."

"_____ this," said Mule, as she gave a book

to Mole. "You are _____. You are my friend,"

Mole said, and she came out.

FLORIDA BENCHMARK LA.A.1.1.2: The student identifies words and constructs meaning from text, illustrations, graphics, and charts using the strategies of phonics, word structure, and context clues.

44

Name _____

▶ **Write the word that best completes each sentence.**

| boy | brought | few | head | read |

_____

1. This _____ won the contest!

2. He was standing on his _____ for a long time.

3. He _____ a book at the same time.

4. He even ate a _____ crackers.

5. Who _____ the boy his prize?

FLORIDA BENCHMARK LA.A.1.1.3: The student uses knowledge of appropriate grade-, age-, and developmental-level vocabulary in reading.

45

Practice Book
Gather Around • Lesson 6

Name _____

▶ **Write the word from the box that names each picture.**

| bike | cone | cube | gate | mule | tube |

1.

_____

- - - - - - - - - - - - - - -

_____

2.

_____

- - - - - - - - - - - - - - -

_____

3.

_____

- - - - - - - - - - - - - - -

_____

4.

_____

- - - - - - - - - - - - - - -

_____

5.

_____

- - - - - - - - - - - - - - -

_____

6.

_____

- - - - - - - - - - - - - - -

_____

FLORIDA BENCHMARK LA.A.1.1.2: The student identifies words and constructs meaning from text, illustrations, graphics, and charts using the strategies of phonics, word structure, and context clues.

46

Practice Book
Gather Around • Lesson 6

Name _____

▶ **Choose the word that finishes each sentence. Write it on the line.**

plan   planned   planning
_____

- -

1. I had _____ to go to bed.

---

wagged   wag   wagging
_____

- -

2. My dog was _____ his tail.

---

tapped   tap   tapping
_____

- -

3. Who is _____ at the door?

---

hugging   hug   hugged
_____

- -

4. I _____ my grandma at the door.

FLORIDA BENCHMARK LA.A.1.1.2: The student identifies words and constructs meaning from text, illustrations, graphics, and charts using the strategies of phonics, word structure, and context clues.

47

© Harcourt

Name _____

▶ **Read the words. Then read the name of
each group. Write each word in the group
where it belongs.**

**Spelling
Words**

lead
head
bread
read
ready
heavy
rule
use
few
boy

Words With <u>ea</u>

_____   _____

_____   _____

_____   _____

_____   _____

_____   _____

Words Without <u>ea</u>

_____   _____

_____   _____

_____   _____

FLORIDA BENCHMARK LA.B.1.1.3: The student produces final
simple documents that have been edited for correct spelling;
appropriate end punctuation; correct capitalization of initial words,
"I," and names of people; correct sentence structure; and correct
usage of age-appropriate verb/subject and noun/pronoun agreement.

▲48▲

Practice Book
Gather Around • Lesson 7

© Harcourt

Name _____

▶ **Finish each sentence. Circle the word that makes sense and has the same vowel sound as the underlined word. Then write the word.**

feather
bread
meat

1. I <u>fed</u> the bird. I gave it some

_____

‒ ‒ ‒ ‒ ‒ ‒ ‒ ‒ ‒ ‒ ‒ ‒ ‒ ‒ ‒

_____ .

meal
breakfast
breath

2. I like to <u>help</u>. Today I made

_____

‒ ‒ ‒ ‒ ‒ ‒ ‒ ‒ ‒ ‒ ‒ ‒ ‒ ‒ ‒

_____ .

breakfast
heat
weather

3. I'll go with <u>them</u> even in bad

_____

‒ ‒ ‒ ‒ ‒ ‒ ‒ ‒ ‒ ‒ ‒ ‒ ‒ ‒ ‒

_____ .

instead
real
head

4. I sleep in my <u>bed</u>.
My bird rests on the sand

_____

‒ ‒ ‒ ‒ ‒ ‒ ‒ ‒ ‒ ‒ ‒ ‒ ‒ ‒ ‒

_____ .

FLORIDA BENCHMARK LA.A.1.1.2: The student identifies words and
constructs meaning from text, illustrations, graphics, and charts
using the strategies of phonics, word structure, and context clues.

49

Practice Book
Gather Around • Lesson 7

▶ **Write go or went to complete each**
   sentence. Then circle now or in the past to show
   when each action took place.

_____
- - - - - - - - - - - - - - -

1. You and I can _____ to   **now**
      the zoo.   **in the past**

_____
- - - - - - - - - - - - - - -

2. We _____ last month.   **now**
                                             in the past

_____
- - - - - - - - - - - - - - -

3. We can _____ again.   **now**
                                             in the past

_____
- - - - - - - - - - - - - - -

4. The goats _____   **now**
      from rock to rock last time.   **in the past**

TRY
THIS

Work with a partner to change each sentence. If it is in
the past, make it tell about now. If it is about now, make
it tell about something in the past. Use the words <u>go</u>
and <u>went</u>.

© Harcourt

FLORIDA BENCHMARK LA.B.1.1.3: The student produces final
simple documents that have been edited for correct spelling;
appropriate end punctuation; correct capitalization of initial words,
"I," and names of people; correct sentence structure; and correct
usage of age-appropriate verb/subject and noun/pronoun agreement.

50

Practice Book
Gather Around • Lesson 7

Name _____

▶ **Read the sentences. Do what they tell you. Circle the words that have the /e/ vowel sound.**

What Is Up Ahead?

1. It has feathers. Color the feathers blue.

2. Its web is spread between the branches. Color it red.

3. It is heavy and has a huge head. Color it gray.

4. It looks like bad weather. Color the storm clouds.

5. A big animal is taking a bath. Color it green.

 TRY THIS Make funny or scary warning signs. Each one should include the word <u>ahead</u>.

FLORIDA BENCHMARK LA.A.1.1.2: The student identifies words and constructs meaning from text, illustrations, graphics, and charts using the strategies of phonics, word structure, and context clues.

51

Practice Book
Gather Around • Lesson 7

Name _____

▶ **Write the word from the box that best completes each sentence.**

afternoon	bicycle	carry	hours	parents

1. I have a new _____ .

2. We can _____

it on the back of our car.

3. My _____ and I

like to ride together.

4. We can ride for _____!

5. I hope we can go riding this _____ .

FLORIDA BENCHMARK LA.A.1.1.3: The student uses knowledge of appropriate grade-, age-, and developmental-level vocabulary in reading.

52

Practice Book
Gather Around • Lesson 7

© Harcourt

Name _____

▶ **Circle the word that names the picture.**
Then write the word.

1.

third   thud   thread

_____

- - - - - - - - - - -

_____

2.

bead   bad   bed

_____

- - - - - - - - - - -

_____

3.

ten   ton   teen

_____

- - - - - - - - - - -

_____

4.

had   head   help

_____

- - - - - - - - - - -

_____

5.

bird   bread   broth

_____

- - - - - - - - - - -

_____

6.

weep   when   web

_____

- - - - - - - - - - -

_____

FLORIDA BENCHMARK LA.A.1.1.2: The student identifies words and
constructs meaning from text, illustrations, graphics, and charts
using the strategies of phonics, word structure, and context clues.

53

Practice Book
Gather Around • Lesson 7

Name _____

▶ **Read the selection. Circle the main idea
and write four details. Write one detail on each rock.**

In 1997, people learned a lot about Mars from a
robot. A robot car called Rover traveled to Mars.
The Rover's job was to collect facts about Mars.
The Rover picked up rocks. It took pictures. It
collected facts about the weather on Mars.

Things the Rover Did

 TRY THIS Make up your own title for the selection.

FLORIDA BENCHMARK LA.A.2.1.1: The student determines the
main idea or essential message from text and identifies supporting
information.

54

Practice Book
Gather Around • Lesson 7

© Harcourt

Name _____

► **Put the two word parts together. Double the last letter before you add _ed_ or _ing_. Write the word to complete the sentence.**

stop + ed

_____

- -

1. The bus has _____ .

get + ing

_____

- -

2. Many people are _____ on.

put + ing

_____

- -

3. That man is _____ his big bag on the shelf.

drop + ed

_____

- -

4. Oh no! He _____ it!

step + ing

_____

- -

5. Who is _____ on my sneaker?

FLORIDA BENCHMARK LA.A.1.1.2: The student identifies words and constructs meaning from text, illustrations, graphics, and charts using the strategies of phonics, word structure, and context clues.

55

Practice Book
Gather Around • Lesson 7

▶ **Read the words. Then read the name of each group. Write each word in the group where it belongs.**

Words With <u>ool</u>

_____

_ _ _ _ _ _ _ _ _ _ _ _ _

_____

_____

Words With <u>oot</u>

_____

_ _ _ _ _ _ _ _ _ _ _ _ _

_____

_____

Words With <u>ooth</u>

_____

_ _ _ _ _ _ _ _ _ _ _ _ _

_____

_____

Words Without <u>oo</u>

_____

_ _ _ _ _ _ _ _ _ _ _ _ _

_____

_____

_____

_ _ _ _ _ _ _ _ _ _ _ _ _

_____

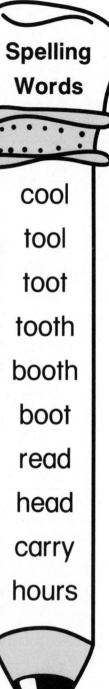

Spelling Words

cool

tool

toot

tooth

booth

boot

read

head

carry

hours

© Harcourt

FLORIDA BENCHMARK LA.B.1.1.3: The student produces final simple documents that have been edited for correct spelling; appropriate end punctuation; correct capitalization of initial words, "I," and names of people; correct sentence structure; and correct usage of age-appropriate verb/subject and noun/pronoun agreement.

56

Practice Book
Gather Around • Lesson 8

Name _____

▶ **Write the word from the box that best completes each sentence.**

broom	food	noon	soon	spoon

_____

1. It's almost _____.

_____

2. Our friends will be here _____.

_____

3. Bring the _____ so I can sweep.

_____

4. Is the _____ ready?

_____

5. Use this big _____ to stir it.

FLORIDA BENCHMARK LA.A.1.1.2: The student identifies words and constructs meaning from text, illustrations, graphics, and charts using the strategies of phonics, word structure, and context clues.

59

Practice Book
Gather Around • Lesson 8

▶ **Write the word from the box that best completes each sentence.**

| against | shook | fire | quietly | careful |

_____

1. We made a _____ in our camp.

_____

2. We were _____
to make our fire safe.

_____

3. We sat _____ and watched it.

_____

4. I leaned _____ my dad.

_____

5. A\ er a while, he _____ me awake.

FLORIDA BENCHMARK A.1.1.3: The student uses knowledge of
appropriate grade-, age-, developmental-level vocabulary in
reading.

60

Practice Book
Gather Around • Lesson 8

© Harcourt

Name _____

► Circle the word that names the picture.
Then write the word.

1.

boot   boat   bat

_____

- - - - - - - - - - - - - -

_____

2.

boot   boat   bat

_____

- - - - - - - - - - - - - -

_____

3.

tool   tooth   toad

_____

- - - - - - - - - - - - - -

_____

4.

tool   tooth   toad

_____

- - - - - - - - - - - - - -

_____

5.

roots   rods   roads

_____

- - - - - - - - - - - - - -

_____

6.

roots   rods   roads

_____

- - - - - - - - - - - - - -

_____

© Harcourt

FLORIDA BENCHMARK LA.A.1.1.2: The student identifies words and constructs meaning from text, illustrations, graphics, and charts using the strategies of phonics, word structure, and context clues.

61

Practice Book
Gather Around • Lesson 8

Name _____

▶ **Read the story. Then finish the sentences about the story.**

One day Nick went to play with his friend Lexa. "Do you want to make a sandwich?" she asked him.

"First we need bread," she told Nick. Nick and Lexa put bread on their plates.

"Next we need peanut butter. Spread the peanut butter on the bread," said Lexa. They did.

"Now we need jelly," said Lexa. "Spread the jelly on the peanut butter."

"It looks good," said Nick. "Now what?"

"Now we eat!" said Lexa. And they did.

_____

1. Lexa showed Nick how to make a _____.

2. Just before they spread the jelly, Lexa and

_____

Nick spread the _____.

3. The last thing Lexa and Nick did was _____.

© Harcourt

Name _____

► **Read the words in the box. Write the word that completes each clue.**

| boot | broom | hoot | room | root | zoom |

_____

- - - - - - - - - - - -

1. I say _____.

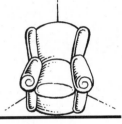

_____

- - - - - - - - - - - -

2. I sit in the corner of a _____.

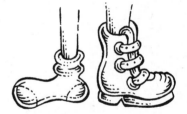

_____

- - - - - - - - - - - -

3. I need a _____.

_____

- - - - - - - - - - - -

4. I can _____.

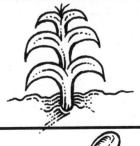

_____

- - - - - - - - - - - -

5. I have a long _____.

_____

- - - - - - - - - - - -

6. You use me with a _____.

FLORIDA BENCHMARK LA.A.1.1.2: The student identifies words and constructs meaning from text, illustrations, graphics, and charts using the strategies of phonics, word structure, and context clues.

Practice Book
Gather Around • Lesson 8

© Harcourt

The Long Flight

1

3

Blue Bird thought he
would try a long flight.

— Fold —

— Fold —

Blue Bird found a
wonderful warm home.

8

Blue Bird flew a long time.
The sky got lighter and lighter.

6

4

The winter grew chilly. Other birds joined him as he flew.

2

Blue Bird grew and grew. It was time to learn to fly.

The days got brighter and brighter.

7

Sometimes there was nothing to eat. Blue Bird was not afraid.

5

Frog and Mouse

1

Mouse could not stay and play. He hurried off to work.

3

Then the two played near the woods.

8

"Make sure you get set for winter. Then you may play."

6

2

One gray night Frog wanted to play with Mouse.

4

Winter was near. Mouse did not want to be caught in the cold without a home.

7

Frog helped Mouse until the job was finished.

5

His father always said, "Son, find a winter home."

Find Something to Do

My tower crashes. My mom says, "Find something different to do."

How do you find something to do?

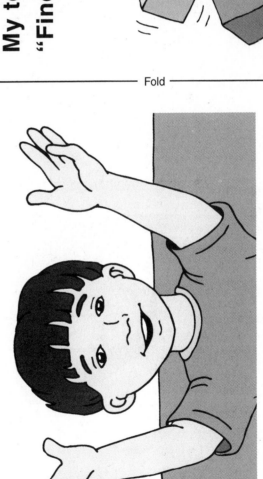

Of course I want to help. This is something to do.

Practice Book
Gather Around • Cut-out Fold-up Book

2
During a rainstorm, my mom says, "Find something to do."

— Fold —

© Harcourt

4
I run like a wild animal.
My mom says, "Listen, child,
you need to mind."

— Fold —

5
"Are you ready to help
with these cookies?"

7
This cookie is big
enough for both of us.

Old Rover

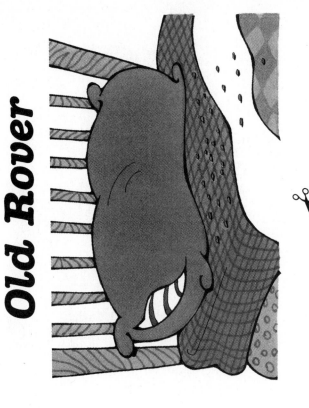

1

"Do you want toast?" asked Jake.

3

Rover didn't stop. He ate the jam and toast. Now we will have to clean the floor!

8

Jake came in with the toast. Rover went to see.

9

© Harcourt

2

I was sick and in my bed.
I had a bad cold.

4

"Yes, a piece of toast with jam, please," I said.

Fold

© Harcourt

Fold

Rover sniffed and jumped all over the bed. "Stop!" I said.

7

Rover jumped up and pulled the blanket. I scolded him.

5

Gather Around • Cut-out Fold-up Book

72

The Bridge

1

Fold

Three goats went to cross the bridge. The little goat said they'd be okay.

3

"Here's a page of notes. Don't budge until you fix this bridge," said the goat.

8

Fold

"I'm sorry, Troll, but this rail is not safe," said the goat.

6

2
An angry troll made a pledge. "This is my bridge. No one will cross it."

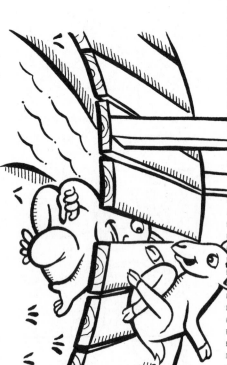

4
"Stay off my bridge!" said the troll. "I'd better," said the goat. "You have a lot of work to do."

Fold

© Harcourt

Fold

7
"Just look at this hole! I nearly fell. You should take better care of your bridge."

5
"You're kidding," said the troll. "Look at this edge," said the goat. "It needs paint."

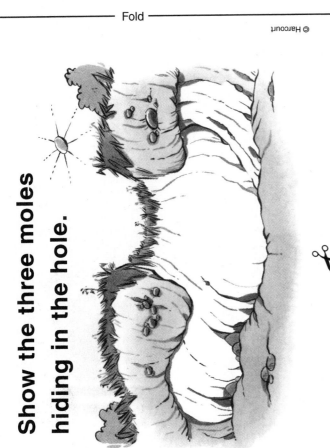

Three Moles and a Mule

1

3

"I'd be careful if I were you," he said. "Snake can hide in the grass."

© Harcourt

— Fold —

— Fold —

Show the three moles hiding in the hole.

8

"You're rude, Mule," said the little moles.

6

Practice Book
Gather Around • Cut-out Fold-up Book

"We are not afraid," the moles said.

An old mule saw three cute moles near the edge of a hole.

The old mule said, "Snake can move fast. He looks like a long tube."

"I want to help. Go find a safe place to hide," said Mule.

1

Ready for

Space

✂

3

If I could, I'd leave right now and head for the stars.

© Harcourt

Fold ——— Fold

8

I'd wave to my parents on Earth.

✂

6

When I got there, I'd get ready for a walk. What would I see?

Practice Book
Gather Around • Cut-out Fold-up Book

Sometimes I sit for hours and think about space.

2

Fold

What could I carry back?
What would I do?

7

© Harcourt

Fold

4

I'd leave in the afternoon.

I wonder if I could bring my bicycle. No, not to space.

5

Fold

Who do you think will win?

ZOO RACE

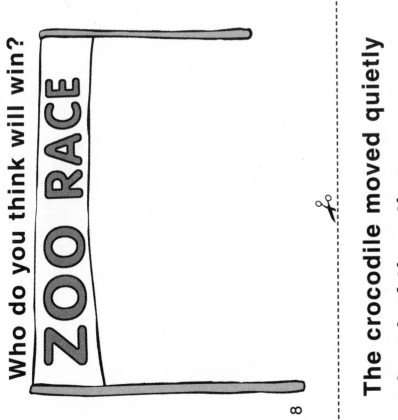

8

ZOO RACE

1

Fold

The crocodile moved quietly ahead of the others.

6

The baboon soon led the way. 3

Fold

The ostrich shook her feathers and ran against the wind.

Get ready. Get set. Go!

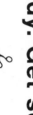

Fold

Fold

Don't be fooled by his size. The rhinoceros ran quickly over the mud.

Be careful, everyone. The gazelle is ahead now.

Skills and Strategies Index

COMPREHENSION

Classifying **L4** 22, 30, 53

Literary Elements: Plot **L5** 8, 39, 62

Main Idea **L5** 23, 31, 54

GRAMMAR

Contractions with *Not* **L5** 58

Describing Words: Color, Size, Shape **L4** 42

Describing Words: *-er, -est* **L5** 4

Describing Words: Feelings **L4** 34

Describing Words: How Many **L4** 57

Describing Words: Taste, Smell, Sound, and Feel **L4** 49

Describing Words: Weather **L4** 65

Names of Holidays **L4** 10

Using *Am*, *Is*, and *Are* **L5** 27

Using *Go* and *Went* **L5** 50

Using *He, She, It*, and *They* **L4** 26

Using *I* and *Me* **L4** 18

Using *Was* and *Were* **L5** 43

Verbs **L5** 12

Verbs That Tell About Now **L5** 19

Verbs That Tell About the Past **L5** 35

PHONICS

Consonants

/j/g, *dge* **L5** 34, 36

/s/c **L4** 41, 43

Contractions

's, n't, 'll **L4** 15, 39, 62

've, 'd, 're **L5** 32, 40

Inflections

-ed, -ing **L4** 23, **L5** 9, 16, 24, 47, 55

-es, -ed, -ing **L4** 31

Initial Blends with *l* L4 69

Long Vowels

/ā/*a-e* **L4** 17, 19

/ā/*ai, ay* **L5** 11, 13

/ē/*e, ee, ea* **L4** 9, 11

/ē/*y* **L4** 25, 27

/ī/*i* **L5** 18, 20

/ī/*i-e* **L4** 33, 35

/ī/*igh* **L5** 3, 5

/ī/*y, ie* **L4** 56, 58, 60

/ō/*o* **L5** 26, 28

/ō/*o-e* **L4** 64, 66

/(y)o͞o/*u-e* **L5** 42, 44

Skills and Strategies Index

Phonograms
  -ice, ide **L4** 46
  -oom, -oot **L5** 63
  -own, -ound **L4** 54

Short Vowels
  /e/*ea* **L5** 49, 51

Vowel Variants
  /o͞o/*oo* **L5** 57, 59
  /ou/*ow, ou* **L4** 48, 50

CVVC-CVVCC Words (with *ee, ea, ow, oa*) **L4** 13
CVC-CVCe Words (*a, a-e*) **L4** 21
CVCCy-CCVCCy Words **L4** 29
CVC-CVCe Words (with *i, i-e*) **L4** 37
CVC-CVCe Words (with *o, o-e*) **L4** 68
CVCe-CCVCe Words (with *ace, ice*) **L4** 45
CCVVC Words (with *ou, ow*) **L4** 52

CVVC and *–igh* Words **L5** 7
CVV-CVVC-CVCe Words (*ai, ay, a-e*) **L5** 15
CVCe-CVCC Words (with *i-e, i*) **L5** 22
CVCe-CVCC Words (with *o-e, o*) **L5** 30
CVCe-CVCCe Words (with *ge, dge*) **L5** 38
CVCe Words (with *u-e, a-e, i-e, o-e*) **L5** 46
CVC-CVVC Words (*e, ea*) **L5** 53
CVVC-CVVCC Words (*oo, oa*) **L5** 61

SPELLING
  L4 8, 16, 24, 32, 40, 47, 55, 63
  L5 2, 10, 17, 25, 33, 41, 48, 56

STUDY SKILL
  Alphabetical Order **L4** 14, 38, 61

VOCABULARY
  L4 12, 20, 28, 36, 44, 51, 59, 67
  L5 6, 14, 21, 29, 37, 45, 52, 60

· TROPHIES ·

End-of-Selection Tests

Grade 1

Name _____ Date _____

A Bed Full of Cats

Directions: Fill in the circle by the correct answer.

Sample   Can you _____ a story?
- ◯ write
- ◯ room
- ◯ who

Vocabulary

1. We can play in my _____.
- ◯ door
- ◯ room
- ◯ great

2. They _____ to a new house.
- ◯ know
- ◯ made
- ◯ moved

3. He _____ try to find the rope.
- ◯ place
- ◯ should
- ◯ follow

A Bed Full of Cats

4. Do you _____ your way to school?

- ◯ know
- ◯ anything
- ◯ kind

5. We have _____ big fish in the pond.

- ◯ too
- ◯ only
- ◯ also

Comprehension

6. Flora is gone so Lee_____ .

- ◯ looks for her
- ◯ likes it that way
- ◯ wiggles his fingers

7. Grandma said, "Flora will come home when she _____ ."

- ◯ is sad
- ◯ needs to eat
- ◯ wants to play

8. Lee put an ad _____ .

- ◯ at school
- ◯ in the garden
- ◯ in the newspaper

© Harcourt

Practice Book
Time Together

A Bed Full of Cats

9. Lee felt _____ .

◯ sad

◯ tall

◯ surprised

Directions: Draw or write the answer to the question.

10. What did Flora have with her when she came home?

_____

- -

_____

- -

_____

Directions: Fill in the circle by the correct answer.

Sample Can you find your _____ on the map?
- ◯ sometimes
- ◯ town
- ◯ door

Vocabulary

1. The _____ is a big place.
- ◯ world
- ◯ would
- ◯ together

2. Put those books _____ there.
- ◯ other
- ◯ over
- ◯ also

3. They have a _____ surprise for Dad.
- ◯ special
- ◯ soon
- ◯ many

© Harcourt

4. _____ looks beautiful from space.
- ◯ Every
- ◯ Each
- ◯ Earth

5. My friends come from a _____ that is a long way away.
- ◯ where
- ◯ country
- ◯ day

Comprehension

6. What can you find on a town map?
- ◯ streets
- ◯ countries
- ◯ rooms

7. On a map of the United States you can find _____.
- ◯ schools
- ◯ streets
- ◯ states

8. The Earth is like a _____.
- ◯ flat place
- ◯ beautiful night
- ◯ giant ball

© Harcourt

Me on the Map

9. Everyone has their own _____ on a map.

○ new friend

○ special place

○ play room

Directions: Draw or write the end to the sentence.

10. I can use a map to find _____.

Directions: Fill in the circle by the correct answer.

Sample   The _____ house has big rooms.
   ○ some
   ○ people
   ○ old

Vocabulary

1. There are _____ kinds of houses around the world.
   ○ different
   ○ moved
   ○ together

2. Her cat is four _____ old.
   ○ kind
   ○ years
   ○ tall

3. The sun is _____ in the day time.
   ○ too
   ○ warm
   ○ soft

© Harcourt

4. Some people like to live in a boat on the _____.
- ◯ water
- ◯ want
- ◯ where

5. Will you _____ my book?
- ◯ help
- ◯ here
- ◯ hold

Comprehension

6. One kind of shelter is a _____.
- ◯ chick
- ◯ house
- ◯ friend

7. Many people can live together in _____.
- ◯ apartment houses
- ◯ one room
- ◯ a tent

8. A house on stilts keeps the house _____.
- ◯ in the ice
- ◯ on the sand
- ◯ above water

© Harcourt

9. What can a house on wheels do?
- ◯ float on water
- ◯ move around
- ◯ sit in sand

Directions: Draw or write the answer to the question.

10. What are three different kinds of houses?

Directions: Fill in the circle by the correct answer.

Sample   My _____ door is red.
   ◯ hold
   ◯ front
   ◯ above

Vocabulary

1. Do you know how to _____?
   ◯ cook
   ◯ moved
   ◯ sometimes

2. A chick is a _____ hen.
   ◯ big
   ◯ young
   ◯ tall

3. They like the cat story the _____.
   ◯ now
   ◯ many
   ◯ most

4. We can help _____ there are many things
to cook.
- ◯ because
- ◯ listen
- ◯ why

5. He can _____ the big city.
- ◯ different
- ◯ picture
- ◯ listen

Comprehension

6. Camila wants Abuelita to tell a story
about _____.
- ◯ long ago
- ◯ animals
- ◯ her father

7. What did they use to cook with when Abuelita
was little?
- ◯ rope
- ◯ coal
- ◯ food

Tell Me a Story

8. What did Abuelita and her friends like to do most?
   - ○ jump rope
   - ○ read stories
   - ○ fly kites

9. Abuelita wished she could sail _____.
   - ○ all the way to the sea
   - ○ around the world
   - ○ to a beautiful island

Practice Book
Time Together

Directions: Draw or write the answer to the question.

10. What could Abuelita see in the river by her abuelita's house?

_____

- -

_____

_____

- -

_____

Name _____ Date _____

My Robot

Directions: Fill in the circle by the correct answer.

Sample It is _____ time for school.
- ◯ because
- ◯ pretty
- ◯ almost

Vocabulary

1. Can you hear the _____ on the TV now?
- ◯ sound
- ◯ sometimes
- ◯ front

2. What did Bob _____?
- ◯ country
- ◯ say
- ◯ special

3. The robot _____ many things.
- ◯ were
- ◯ don't
- ◯ does

4. Cecil can make _____ cakes.
- ◯ pretty
- ◯ cook
- ◯ once

5. Pam is _____ on time for school.
- ◯ ago
- ◯ above
- ◯ always

Comprehension

6. The robot is _____.
- ◯ Cecil
- ◯ Dennis
- ◯ Prince

7. Cecil is IT when he plays _____.
- ◯ tag
- ◯ hide-and-seek
- ◯ with the dog

8. What does Cecil do for Dad?
- ◯ mows the grass
- ◯ makes a pretty cake
- ◯ cleans his room

My Robot

9. What is the very best thing Cecil does?
- ◯ is a good friend
- ◯ cleans a room
- ◯ leads the school band

Directions: Draw or write the answer to the question.

10. What would you like Cecil to do for you?

_____

- -

_____

_____

- -

_____

Practice Book
Time Together

On the Job with Dr. Martha Smith

Directions: Fill in the circle by the correct answer.

Sample   Do you have _____ pets?
○ always
○ almost
○ any

Vocabulary

1. The man _____ his cats to the vet.
○ that
○ care
○ took

2. My family has _____ cats.
○ eight
○ each
○ any

3. Dan will _____ for the dog.
○ only
○ care
○ could

© Harcourt

A21

On the Job with Dr. Martha Smith

4. Mom is _____ with the baby.
- ○ busy
- ○ but
- ○ boots

5. _____ Martha Smith is a good vet.
- ○ By
- ○ Mr.
- ○ Dr.

Comprehension

6. Dr. Smith is a vet at the _____ .
- ○ big house
- ○ animal shelter
- ○ old town

7. What does Dr. Smith do first each day?
- ○ meets a special cat
- ○ plays with the dogs
- ○ checks new animals

8. Muffin was a _____ .
- ○ lost kitty
- ○ big dog
- ○ special food

© Harcourt

On the Job with Dr. Martha Smith

9. Why does Dr. Smith watch new animals when they come to the shelter?
- ◯ to give them a bath
- ◯ to see if they are healthy
- ◯ to see how they act

Directions: Draw or write the answer to the question.

10. What are three kinds of animals that Dr. Smith gets at the shelter?

_____

- -

_____

- -

_____

Practice Book
Time Together

Directions: Fill in the circle by the correct answer.

Sample   Mom _____ the door for me.
- ◯ only
- ◯ opened
- ◯ helped

Vocabulary

1. The bird sits _____ in the treetop.
- ◯ high
- ◯ how
- ◯ hides

2. My friends always say _____ .
- ◯ hold
- ◯ here
- ◯ hello

3. Little Bear _____ cookies.
- ◯ listened
- ◯ loved
- ◯ walked

4. Can we play together _____ soon?
- ○ again
- ○ also
- ○ above

5. The sea is a pretty _____.
- ○ red
- ○ busy
- ○ blue

Comprehension

6. Little Bear can not play with the squirrels because he has to _____.
- ○ climb the tree
- ○ go home for lunch
- ○ play with Emily

7. The little girl thinks she is _____.
- ○ funny
- ○ lost
- ○ busy

8. Emily wants Little Bear to _____.
- ○ go away
- ○ be her friend
- ○ eat lunch with her

Name _____ Date _____

Little Bear's Friend

9. Where does Emily live?
- ◯ in a tree house
- ◯ in a big town
- ◯ by the river

Directions: Draw or write the answer to the question.

10. What does Little Bear see from the treetop?

_____

- - - - - - - - - - - - - - - - - -

_____

_____

- - - - - - - - - - - - - - - - - -

_____

Practice Book
Time Together

Busy Buzzy Bee

Directions: Fill in the circle by the correct answer.

Sample We can pick _____ flowers.
  ○ warm
  ○ with
  ○ wild

Vocabulary

1. The wild flowers grow in a _____ .
  ○ field
  ○ follow
  ○ family

2. Put _____ cookies in the bag.
  ○ tall
  ○ twelve
  ○ young

3. They will _____ here for their friends.
  ○ wait
  ○ where
  ○ way

Practice Book
Time Together

4. Do you have _____ book?
- ◯ eight
- ◯ other
- ◯ another

5. Don't _____ the warm pan.
- ◯ took
- ◯ touch
- ◯ grow

Comprehension

6. What can the bee find in each flower?
- ◯ hive
- ◯ nectar
- ◯ honey

7. Busy Bee is a _____ bee.
- ◯ queen
- ◯ drone
- ◯ worker

8. Inside the hive, the bees make _____.
- ◯ eggs
- ◯ cells
- ◯ nectar

© Harcourt

9. Grubs change to bees in _____ days.

⬭ four

⬭ nine

⬭ twelve

Directions: Draw or write the answer to the question.

10. What happens to grubs inside the cells?

Practice Book
Time Together

Name _____ Date _____

Directions: Fill in the circle by the correct answer.

Sample The little bird _____ from the nest to the tree.
- ○ flew
- ○ walked
- ○ joined

Vocabulary

1. I _____ you had fed the animals.
- ○ talked
- ○ thought
- ○ touched

2. Do you _____ where the bird is?
- ○ took
- ○ would
- ○ wonder

3. Some birds are _____ of cats.
- ○ afraid
- ○ away
- ○ almost

© Harcourt

Practice Book
Gather Around

4. There is _____ in the bag.
- ◯ almost
- ◯ nothing
- ◯ night

5. The little bird will _____ to fly.
- ◯ learn
- ◯ listen
- ◯ thought

Comprehension

6. While the other birds test their wings, the little blue bird watches because he is _____ .
- ◯ young
- ◯ afraid
- ◯ warm

7. When the blue bird wants to know what is out there, the mother bird says, "_____ ."
- ◯ Many things
- ◯ Anything
- ◯ Nothing

8. Who does the little bird fly with first?
- ◯ red bird
- ◯ green bird
- ◯ mother bird

© Harcourt

Practice Book
Gather Around

The Story of a Blue Bird

9. Once the blue bird flies, he is not _____.

○ sad

○ funny

○ afraid

Directions: Draw or write the answer to the question.

10. Who does the blue bird fly with at the end of the story?

Directions: Fill in the circle by the correct answer.

Sample They are wet because they were _____ in the rain.
- ○ caught
- ○ near
- ○ flew

Vocabulary

1. They _____ so they would not get too wet.
- ○ thought
- ○ hurried
- ○ happily

2. Their house is _____ the field.
- ○ about
- ○ over
- ○ near

3. Dan is the man's _____.
- ○ sister
- ○ son
- ○ mom

© Harcourt

Frog and Toad All Year

4. Are you _____ it is raining?
- ○ sure
- ○ always
- ○ only

5. This is a _____, wet day.
- ○ water
- ○ old
- ○ cold

Comprehension

6. Toad stands by the stove _____.
- ○ to eat tea and cake
- ○ to dry his clothes
- ○ because the day is spoiled

7. A young frog is called a _____.
- ○ chick
- ○ pollywog
- ○ fish

8. Where does Frog's father tell him to look for spring?
- ○ around the corner
- ○ along the river
- ○ in the river

© Harcourt

Practice Book
Gather Around

9. When it stops raining, Frog and Toad _____.
- ◯ find winter
- ◯ find a worm
- ◯ find spring

Directions: Draw or write the answer to the question.

10. When the rain stopped, Frog and Toad rushed outside. What do you think they found?

Name _____ Date _____

Directions: Fill in the circle by the correct answer.

Sample   My friends grow _____ corn and flowers in their garden.
   ◯ always
   ◯ but
   ◯ both

Vocabulary

1. Jan is _____ to go.
   ◯ ready
   ◯ almost
   ◯ right

2. We don't play outside _____ the storm.
   ◯ above
   ◯ during
   ◯ from

Comprehension

3. How many toes does a brown bear have?
   ◯ five
   ◯ four
   ◯ two

© Harcourt

Practice Book
Gather Around

Fishing Bears

4. Brown bears live near water so they can
_____ .

○ play tag
○ find food
○ stand up

5. Baby bears are called _____ .
○ chicks
○ pups
○ cubs

6. How is the walk of a brown bear different from other furry animals?
○ Brown bears walk on their toes.
○ Brown bears put their feet down flat.
○ Brown bears run and hop.

7. Brown bears eat _____ .
○ only fish
○ both plants and animals
○ only clams and salmon

8. How do bears get ready for winter?
○ They take a nap.
○ They eat a lot.
○ They make a den.

© Harcourt

Practice Book
Gather Around

9. When bears hibernate, they are _____ .

◯ very cold

◯ in a deep sleep

◯ fishing for food

Directions: Draw or write the answer to the question.

10. How many cubs does a mother bear usually have?

How to Be a Nature Detective

Directions: Fill in the circle by the correct answer.

Sample   A _____ likes to find answers to questions.
○ diver
○ detective
○ teacher

Vocabulary

1. Look where you walk because the _____ is wet.
○ floor
○ whistle
○ house

2. Take that _____ of cake.
○ people
○ piece
○ day

3. It is fun to learn about _____.
○ nothing
○ helps
○ nature

© Harcourt

How to Be a Nature Detective

4. The bird _____ up a big worm.
- ○ feels
- ○ fills
- ○ pulls

5. Detectives look for _____.
- ○ friends
- ○ clues
- ○ toes

Comprehension

6. Where can a nature detective look for clues?
- ○ almost anywhere
- ○ only in the river
- ○ only in a tree

7. A cat does not leave claw marks because a cat _____.
- ○ does not have any claws
- ○ walks on only two of its paws
- ○ pulls its claws in when it walks

8. The tracks of a sea gull tell you _____.
- ○ where the wind was coming from
- ○ how old the gull is
- ○ when the gull was on the beach

© Harcourt

How to Be a Nature Detective

9. Gulls are like airplanes because they _____ .
  ○ take off at night
  ○ make funny sounds
  ○ take off facing the wind

Directions: Draw or write the answer to the question.

10. What is another place a nature detective can look for clues?

Directions: Fill in the circle by the correct answer.

Sample It is _____ time to go to bed.
- ◯ fly
- ◯ away
- ◯ nearly

Vocabulary

1. Bob is _____ he can't find the book you want.
- ◯ almost
- ◯ pretty
- ◯ sorry

2. It is _____ for you to sit here.
- ◯ okay
- ◯ once
- ◯ over

3. Turtle got _____ when elephant splashed him.
- ◯ tall
- ◯ angry
- ◯ young

Comprehension

4. He asks his mother if he can _____ .
- ◯ play in the puddles
- ◯ sail his boat in the puddles
- ◯ sail his boat in the river

5. He put on _____ to go outside.
- ◯ boots
- ◯ a scarf
- ◯ a smile

6. What does the alligator offer to do?
- ◯ have tea with frog
- ◯ get the boat back
- ◯ swim with turtle

7. What does Pig do?
- ◯ splash water
- ◯ sail the boat
- ◯ swim in the puddle

8. The _____ drank up the puddle.
- ◯ elephant
- ◯ alligator
- ◯ turtle

9. When the sun comes out, _____.

○ the animals play tag

○ the puddle dries up

○ the animals take the boat

Directions: Draw or write the answer to the question.

10. What is the story about?

Name _____ Date _____

Directions: Fill in the circle by the correct answer.

Sample The _____ is ten years old.
- ◯ boy
- ◯ man
- ◯ saleslady

Vocabulary

1. They _____ a box of surprises to school.
- ◯ listened
- ◯ worked
- ◯ brought

2. Here are a _____ flowers for you.
- ◯ few
- ◯ field
- ◯ trees

3. Dan put a blue hat on his _____.
- ◯ nose
- ◯ head
- ◯ foot

A53

4. Have you _____ both story books?
- ◯ read
- ◯ answered
- ◯ hurried

Comprehension

5. Poppleton wants a new bed because his is _____ .
- ◯ new
- ◯ old
- ◯ grown-up

6. The saleslady took Poppleton to try _____ .
- ◯ four beds
- ◯ the softest bed
- ◯ the biggest bed

7. When the saleslady gets Poppleton a book, he looks at _____ .
- ◯ TV
- ◯ the pictures
- ◯ a few pages

8. Next, Poppleton wants _____ .
- ◯ cookies
- ◯ crackers
- ◯ water

Poppleton Everyday

9. The last thing Poppleton asks for is _____ .

○ a game
○ some food
○ bluebirds

Directions: Draw or write the answer to the question.

10. Why do you think the saleslady says again and again, "Do you want the bed?"

_____

- -

_____

_____

- -

_____

Practice Book
Gather Around

Directions: Fill in the circle by the correct answer.

Sample   The baby takes a nap every _____ .
⃝ year
⃝ afternoon
⃝ hour

Vocabulary

1. My _____ will be home from work soon.
⃝ brain
⃝ thoughts
⃝ parents

2. You can ride my _____ .
⃝ bicycle
⃝ fish
⃝ bear

3. How many _____ do you sleep each night?
⃝ years
⃝ days
⃝ hours

Sleep Is for Everyone

4. We can _____ the box to the front door.
- ◯ climb
- ◯ carry
- ◯ box

Comprehension

5. A chicken's eyelids are different from yours because they _____ .
- ◯ go up when they sleep
- ◯ go down when they sleep
- ◯ have no eyelids

6. How does an elephant sleep?
- ◯ It sits down.
- ◯ It stands up.
- ◯ It curls up.

7. Young people need _____ sleep than grown-ups.
- ◯ more
- ◯ less
- ◯ old

© Harcourt

Practice Book
Gather Around

Sleep Is for Everyone

8. Schoolchildren should have about _____ hours of sleep every night.
- ○ two to three
- ○ ten to twelve
- ○ five to eight

9. The only time your brain rests is when you are _____ .
- ○ asleep
- ○ awake
- ○ walking

Practice Book
Gather Around

Sleep Is for Everyone

Directions: Draw or write the answer to the question.

10. Give one reason why you need rest.

Baboon

Directions: Fill in the circle by the correct answer.

Sample   The ground _____ when the elephants walked by.
  ○ should
  ○ took
  ○ shook

Vocabulary

1. Do not go near the hot _____ .
  ○ special
  ○ fire
  ○ flowers

2. Put my bicycle _____ the house.
  ○ against
  ○ almost
  ○ over

3. Dad did not want to wake us so he walked _____ .
  ○ always
  ○ happily
  ○ quietly

4. Be _____ when you pick up the hot pan.
- ○ careful
- ○ angry
- ○ sorry

Comprehension

5. In the forest Baboon learned that some of the world is _____.
- ○ blue
- ○ green
- ○ red

6. The turtle lets Baboon see the world can be _____.
- ○ fast
- ○ soft
- ○ slow

7. When baboon saw the fire, his mother said _____.
- ○ the world is always hot
- ○ the world is not always hot
- ○ be careful

Practice Book
Gather Around

8. A hungry _____ might try to eat Baboon.
  ○ elephant
  ○ crocodile
  ○ monkey

9. Baboon was afraid of the _____.
  ○ elephants
  ○ gazelle
  ○ rhinoceros

Baboon

Directions: Draw or write the answer to the question.

10. What does Baboon learn about the world from his mother?

Practice Book
Gather Around